# Ethical Issues in Caring

In memory of Hesther Frances

# Ethical Issues in Caring

*Edited by*
Gavin Fairbairn
Susan Fairbairn

# Avebury

Aldershot · Brookfield USA · Hong Kong · Singapore · Sydney

Published by
Avebury
Gower Publishing Company Limited
Gower House
Croft Road
Aldershot
Hants GU11 3HR
England

Gower Publishing Company
Old Post Road
Brookfield
Vermont 05036
USA


**British Library Cataloguing-in-Publication Data**

Ethical issues in caring.
  1. Great Britain. Welfare work. Ethical
aspects
  I. Fairbairn, Gavin, *1950 –*  II. Fairbairn,
Susan, *1947 –*
174'.9362'0941

**Library of Congress Cataloging-in-Publication Data**

Ethical issues in caring / [edited by] Gavin Fairbairn
  and Susan Fairbairn.
    p.  cm.
Based on papers from the Ethical Issues in Caring Conferences
held between 1981 and 1985.
Bibliography: p.
Includes index.
  1. Medical ethics.  2. Nursing ethics.  3. Social service –
Moral and ethical aspects.  I. Fairbairn, Gavin.  II. Fairbairn,
Susan.  III. Ethical Issues in Caring Conference.
R724.E7877 1988
174'.2– –dc19                        88-5400
                                          CIP

ISBN 0 566 05266 0


Printed and bound in Great Britain at
The Camelot Press Ltd, Southampton

# Contents

# Notes on contributors

Bob Brecher teaches philosophy in the Humanities Department of Brighton Polytechnic and is a member of the Society for Applied Philosophy. He has contributed to, among other journals, *Explorations in Medicine* and the *Journal of Medical Ethics*, and is the author of *Anselm's Argument: the logic of divine existence* (1985).

James M. Brown was born in Dumfries and educated in England and Scotland. He lives with his wife and three daughters in Coleraine where he teaches ethics, including a course for undergraduate nurses, at the University of Ulster. He is author of several articles in philosophical journals and is currently co-writing a book on nursing ethics.

Revd Alastair V. Campbell is Head of the Department of Christian Ethics and Practical Theology, University of Edinburgh. He was the founding Editor of the *Journal of Medical Ethics* and has published numerous books and articles in the fields of pastoral care and medical ethics, including *Moderated Love: A Theology of Professional Care* (SPCK, 1984) and (editor) *A Dictionary of Pastoral Care* (SPCK, 1987). He has recently completed a period as Visiting Professor in Biomedical Ethics in the Medical School of the University of Otago, New Zealand.

Chris Clark is Lecturer in Social Work, University of Edinburgh. His interests include community work, voluntary action, and the relationship of theory, ideology and practice in social interventions. He is currently researching responses to unemployment. He is author with Stewart Asquith of *Social Work and Social Philosophy: a guide for practice*.

Gavin Fairbairn is Senior Lecturer in Education at the North East Wales Institute, Cartrefle, where he teaches philosophy, special education and psychology. From 1971–85 he worked as a teacher and social worker in special education and child, adolescent and adult psychiatry. He has published papers and chapters relating to ethics in social work, nursing and psychology, and has edited, with Susan Fairbairn, *Psychology, Ethics and Change*. He is co-editing a book on moral problems in special education.

Susan Fairbairn is a part-time Research Associate in the Department of Psychiatry at Manchester University, where she is undertaking research on nurses' communication skills with cancer patients. She is a Tutor in Social Psychology for the Open University and teaches part-time in an infants' school in Manchester. She has published in environmental psychology and medical and nursing education and, with Gavin Fairbairn, has edited *Psychology, Ethics and Change.*

Alison Kitson is Project Coordinator, Standards of Care, at the Royal College of Nursing. She was formerly Lecturer at the University of Ulster, where she had been an undergraduate and postgraduate student. Her main interests are theory development in nursing and the measurement of quality of care. Alison Kitson views quality of care as an ethical issue, related to the centrality of the human being and the maintenance of the personal approach within a complex health care delivery system.

Richard Lindley is Lecturer in Philosophy at Bradford University, and a founder member of the Society for Applied Philosophy. He is the author of *Autonomy* (1986). He is currently writing, with a consultant psychiatrist, a book on ethical issues in psychotherapy.

Professor Baroness McFarlane of Llandaff has been Head of the Department of Nursing, University of Manchester, since it was established in 1974. Her major contribution has been in the conceptual and theoretical analysis of nursing and its identity as a caring profession. Her research has been into the quality of care and the nursing process.

Professor Peter Mittler worked as an NHS clinical psychologist for ten years, specialising in mental handicap and autism, before becoming a lecturer in developmental psychology at Birkbeck College, University of London, where he studied language development and delay, especially in twins. He was appointed first Director of the Hester Adrian Research Centre for the study of learning processes in the mentally handicapped at Manchester University. Since 1982 he has been Professor of Special Education in the Department of Education. He is a former advisor on mental handicap to the Secretary of State for Social Services and is currently consultant in special education to UN agencies. He is immediate past President of the International League of Societies for Persons with Mental Handicap.

Trevor Owen worked for ICI for almost twenty-five years before becoming Managing Director of Remploy in 1978. He is involved in a number of external activities and is currently on the Council of the CBI and Chairman of the National Institute for Social Work.

Edgar Page is Lecturer in Philosophy in the University of Hull. He read economics and then philosophy at Newcastle upon Tyne and then went on to Christ Church, Oxford. He has taught philosophy at Balliol College and Trinity College, Oxford, at the University of Ghana and at the University of Delaware, USA. He is married and has three daughters.

Rod Sheaff lectures in the Health Services Management Unit of the Department of Social Policy and Social Work, Manchester University. Previously he worked as an administrator in the National Health Service and in the Department of Health. He has research experience both in politics and in health service administration.

David Smail was educated at University College, London, and is District Psychologist for Nottingham Health Authority. He is the author of *Psychotherapy: a personal approach* (1978), and *Illusion and Reality: the meaning of anxiety*.

Brian Thorne is Director of Student Counselling in the University of East Anglia, Norwich, and a leading person-centred therapist in the tradition of Carl Rogers. In 1980 he founded with colleagues the Norwich Centre for Personal and Professional Development, which is both a counselling and a training resource for Norwich and the surrounding area.

Jean Towler recently retired as Director of Midwifery Services in Trafford Health Authority. She is joint author, with Roy Butler-Manuel, of *Modern Obstetrics for Student Midwives*, a standard textbook now in its second edition, and with Joan Bramall of *Midwives in History and Society*. She has published many articles on midwifery, particularly on physiological labour and natural birth. She is regularly invited to address both professional and lay conferences on choices in childbirth.

# Preface

This book has emerged from the Ethical Issues in Caring conferences between the years 1982 and 1986. The contributors to those conferences have helped to make the book even those whose papers for one reason or another do not appear within its covers; our thanks to them all. Our thanks also to John Harris for helping to set up the first EIC conference, which gave birth to the series; to Harry Lesser for helping to organise all five conferences; and to Kath Melia for her involvement in EIC II to V.

The book seeks to draw attention to the moral problems that arise from our need to care and to be cared for. We hope it captures some of the vibrancy and controversy of the conferences for which the original versions of these chapters were written. Its aim is to act as a lubricant in the ongoing and ever more important debate between practitioners in the caring professions, philosophers and others who are concerned with and by these moral problems. Our ambition is that it should help to provoke debate about the moral concerns raised by the contributors and awareness of many issues left untouched. The contributors come from a range of theoretical and practical backgrounds including social work, nursing, counselling, psychotherapy and industrial management, as well as philosophy and Christian ethics. They do not necessarily share beliefs about the nature of caring or about political and moral ideology. What they do share is a concern with the moral problems that arise in caring; and in attempting to state some of those concerns they all contribute to this ongoing debate. We do not seek to endorse or provide simplistic ethical solutions. Rather we want to encourage practitioners to notice the moral problems within their practice. We want to encourage awareness that moral issues are important because, whether we are conscious of them or not, they affect us as individuals.[1] Although the focus is dominantly on professional caring, many of the issues raised will be common to those whose caring is done voluntarily.

All the contributions are concerned with questions of value, with questions about how it is appropriate to regard folk, to treat them, to relate to them, whether as individuals or as part of the groups and communities to which they belong. All contain, whether explicitly or implicitly, beliefs about what it is that is valuable about people's lives. All attempt to make explicit some part of the complex of values that surround the business of caring for others in need. While some, notably those by Chris Clark and Rod Sheaff, are focused at the level of social policy and politics, others have a much more personal focus. For example Alison Kitson discusses the way in which the nurse can help patients to get better by helping them to feel better, and Brian Thorne discusses the conflicts that can arise for therapists between adopting an apparently value-free stance and remaining true to their own values. David Smail begins with a discussion of the role of the psychotherapist which is personally focused, but moves on to make observations with implications at the larger political and social level.

The chapters fall into two main groups. The first, while raising issues of practical importance, focuses largely on conceptual matters. For example, Alastair Campbell is concerned to discuss the nature of professional care as vocation; Rod Sheaff addresses the need for a thorough examination of the basis of health resource allocation in terms of needs and justice; Chris Clark discusses the reasons groups of different political colours might have for adopting the Barclay Committee's recommendations about community social work; and Richard Lindley addresses the difficult questions whether and when it can be caring and respectful of others to intervene paternalistically in their lives. The second group addresses particular, often highly topical, issues. For example, Jean Towler and Gavin Fairbairn discuss the extent to which women should be given choice in pregnancy and childbirth; Edgar Page offers a very thorough analysis of what might constitute a reasonable institution of surrogacy; and Peter Mittler discusses the quality of life disabled people can expect.

Many underlying links and themes which are not immediately apparent may be drawn out of the chapters; often these links make it clear that if the writers concerned were in the same room together the air would be buzzing with disagreement. But then we are concerned to facilitate debate and what better way to do it than by having contributors who would disagree with one another if gathered in one place? Many chapters raise questions about the nature of caring but do this in very different ways. Whereas, for example, Baroness McFarlane is mostly concerned to focus on the nature of care in an individual context, Bob Brecher questions the validity of individualised care. Trevor Owen and Peter Mittler both discuss the need to give disabled people responsibility for their lives and both point out the possibility that professionals can end up doing too much for their clients. Discussions of particular issues also fan out to cover a wide area; for example, although Jim Brown is particularly concerned to discuss the appropriateness of feelings of bereavement for mothers who have lost babies through miscarriage, stillbirth or neonatal death, much of what he says is of relevance to the question what it is to care for, and to demonstrate care for, another person even if one does not share their beliefs.

We hope that non-philosophical readers will find the more philosophical chapters accessible and that by entering into a dialogue with the ideas they contain, will relate the analysis and differentiation they seek to provide, to their own hard won practical experiences and difficulties. Conversely we will be encouraged if philosophers find issues of interest to them in the non-philosophical chapters. Certainly there is much here which should be of interest to moral, social and political philosophers, relating for example to problems of social policy and to topics such as autonomy and paternalism, respect for others, responsibility, accountability and choice, justice and the distinction between needs and wants.

## Note

1 For a more detailed discussion of this point see introduction to *Psychology, Ethics and Change*, S. A. Fairbairn and G. J. Fairbairn, eds (1987), (London, RKP), pp. 8–9. Although we are talking there about clinical psychologists, the point is relevant for all caring practitioners.

Gavin Fairbairn
Susan Fairbairn

Whalley Range
Manchester
August 1987

# Acknowledgements

Professor Mittler's paper, 'Quality of life and services for people with disabilities', originally written for the first EIC conference, was first published in the *Bulletin of the British Psychological Society* (1984), 37, pp. 218–25, and we acknowledge with thanks the permission of the BPS to reprint this version. A shortened version of Alastair Campbell's 'Profession and vocation' appeared in the *Nursing Times* 24–30 April 1985, pp. 24–6.

# 1 Profession and vocation

*Alastair V. Campbell*

## Introduction

Let me begin with a quotation from Martin Luther which may give a warning of what lies ahead. In his *Commentary on the Letter to the Galations*, Luther declares: 'God himself will milk the cows through him whose vocation that is'.[1] Such confidence in the heavenly milkman (or milkmaid?) is characteristic of the grandiosity of theology. Theology attempts to encompass in its theories God, humanity and the universe (including cows). I want to retain this grand scale, speaking about professionalism as a theologian, unapologetically, but not (I hope) dogmatically or unintelligibly. I think that theology has some insights to offer into the nature of modern professionalism; and that these insights, which derive basically from the concept of vocation, can be shared by those who do not necessarily hold a religious belief, Christian or other. I shall be appealing to an awareness, encapsulated in Christian symbolism, to which we all have access on the basis of our common human experience. The *interpretations* which I offer are not, of course, ones on which we will all agree, but I think that theology signals a direction of thought which should not be ignored. It is not self-evident that the language of social science or of philosophy is the only valid way of describing human institutions and relationships.

## The critique of professionalism

Before discussing the concept of vocation I will briefly summarise the debate about the definition and moral status of professionalism which has arisen largely as a result of an extensive literature on the sociology of professions and professionalisation. This century has seen a phenomenal expansion in occupational groups claiming what Becker[2] has called 'the honorific title' profession. As Halmos has documented in *The Faith of the Counsellors*,[3] a decrease in the number of clergy and religious in Britain has been matched by a dramatic increase in the range and number of secular helping professions. (Similar changes can be discerned in other post-industrial societies, though in the USA the persistence of large and influential religious groups complicates the picture.) Perhaps especially interesting is the increased self-consciousness and sense of independence of social workers and nurses, since these 'aspirant professions' have produced a considerable literature on the definitions of their distinctive role in society, in attempts to join the ancient club founded by divinity, law and medicine.[4] Moreover the rise of what Halmos calls the 'personal service professions'[5] is but one relatively small corner of a much wider picture of the burgeoning of professional associations of all kinds – accountants, architects, morticians, law enforcement officers, management consultants, civil engineers, to name but a few.[6] To be recognised as a profession (especially if this can be achieved through a legal process which leads to state registration) is undoubtedly a prime objective for numerous occupational groups. Modern society prizes and rewards *occupational* status more than social origins, religious affiliation or indeed moral rectitude.

The rise of professionalism has been viewed with some cynicism by a number of writers. Richard Titmuss describes professions as 'associations for spreading the gospel of self-importance'; Paul Wilding has described their ethical codes as 'campaign documents in the battle for privilege and power';[7] and there is of course the over-quoted remark of Bernard Shaw in *The Doctor's Dilemma*, that professions are 'conspiracies against the laity'. Underlying these comments there is an awareness that the high-sounding ideals on the basis of which these occupational groups make a claim to reliability and social usefulness may not be all that they at first appear. It was Kant who observed that one cannot be sure that a person is acting out of duty if considerable benefit derives from dutifulness. This is the problem inherent within the claims to professional status: to have a claim accepted is to gain a secure, at least reasonably well-paid and well-respected place in society. Perhaps then the claim is made solely to gain that place!

To pursue this point a little further I shall give the briefest of summaries of three approaches to the phenomenon of professionalism in sociological literature. These may be called the trait approach, the power approach and the functionalist approach.

### The Trait Approach
A dead end. Using the established professions as a norm, this approach attempts to compile a list of special traits which set a professional occupation apart from other occupations. A typical list would include:

(a) An established body of power and skill.
(b) A recognised training, usually of several years duration.
(c) Methods of testing competence and of disciplining members, implemented by the occupational group itself.
(d) A service orientation or 'professional ethic' (a good example of this approach can be found in Carr-Saunders and Wilson).[8]

But such a listing of 'typical' features encounters several difficulties:

1  It fails to account for change and evolution in the concept of professionalism, treating it as though it were a fixed entity rather than an aspect of social change.
2  Its choice of 'established professions' to provide normative traits seems somewhat arbitrary.
3  Its descriptions seem wide enough to include virtually any group which gets itself sufficiently organised and which *claims* ethicality (salesmen, market consultants, political pollsters?). At the same time some of the criteria inevitably exclude some groups which make definite claims to be professions, because they lack occupational independence (for example nurses, social workers).

## The power approach

This second approach tends to take medicine as the model for a modern successful profession (see, for example, Freidson),[9] and it observes that doctors have gained two enviable privileges: a state-enforced *monopoly* of work (through Registration Acts) and a high degree of *autonomy* (in terms of selection, training, accreditation, control of conditions of work and rationing of numbers entering the profession). Added to these obvious socio-economic advantages are the more subtle gains of prestige, respect and public trust. This 'power approach' is especially persuasive in accounting for the ever-increasing professionalisation of society. It does seem unlikely that occupational groups struggle for professional recognition for purely disinterested motives.

## The functionalist approach

A third approach examines the nature of professionalism from a functionalist perspective. This approach asks whether certain occupations require to be practised in a particular way in order to be socially useful. Two features of professional relationships are then identified: 'trustworthiness' and 'affective neutrality'. Trustworthiness is seen to be especially necessary in situations where the recipient of a service is vulnerable (emotionally or physically) and is incapable of gaining sufficient knowledge to recognise malpractice. Doctors, nurses, lawyers, social workers and schoolteachers all deal with people who have the double disadvantage of vulnerability and ignorance of what they need. The professional approach is seen as socially necessary, since it provides some guarantee of consistency and reliability derived from training, colleague control and commitment to ethical ideals. 'Affective neutrality' refers to the necessity for a degree of emotional distance from a person's problems, especially when these are of a kind which the untrained lay person would find too worrying or distressing. Doctors, nurses and lawyers learn to approach blood, violence and death with a calmness which would be unnatural in a friend or relative. Such professionalism is again seen as socially useful or functional.

Of these three theories of professionalism, the 'trait approach' is perhaps the least illuminating, because it lacks historical perspective, seeking to 'freeze' the professions in a form established in previous generations. However it is not so easy to arbitrate between the 'power approach' and the 'functionalist approach'. The former sheds much light on the phenomenon of what could be rather loosely described as the 'professions bandwagon'. But perhaps it is too simple, almost too elegant, to account for all the complex elements that enter into the claim to and the recognition of professional status. People can accrue power in a democratic society only when there is some kind of 'fit' between their claims and what is perceived as socially useful. Thus the power of the clergy has diminished as widespread acceptance of religious assertions about reality has faded. Their place has been taken by the 'new priests', the therapists, social workers and the amazing array of medically-related professions, who offer a service which the majority of the population find both necessary and convincingly effective. As the functionalist analysis suggests, professional power is based on perceived social usefulness. And yet ... and yet ... we are perhaps moving to a new era when the claims to ethicality and effectiveness of these 'new priests' is being more radically questioned. How well-based are their claims to be the disinterested helpers of the vulnerable client? Is the 'service ideal' based on any kind of personal integrity, or is it just part of what has been called 'the rhetoric of self-advancement'? Here we see the tension between the power approach and the functionalist approach and here finally we confront the concept of vocation. It is to the explanation of this concept that I shall devote the rest of this chapter.

### Vocation, gifts and grace

Let me begin with some etymological observations – but with the caution that derivation is not necessarily a reliable guide to current usage. The root of vocation (*vocare*) refers to 'calling', while that of profession (*professio*, *profiteri*) refers to a public declaration, a statement of intention, a vow. I wish to suggest that we should recapture the sense of 'publicly avowed intention' in professionalism and that this can usefully be related to the notion of a calling to use one's unmerited abilities in a specific way.

In order to give some substance to this rather formal definition, I must now make reference to three theological doctrines: creation, fall and redemption. A religious view of the world (at least from the Jewish and Christian perspectives) regards it as mirroring, though in a partial and distorted fashion, the intentions of a benevolent creator, who wishes to see the flourishing and fulfilment of all created things in a manner which safeguards their essential nature. For both human and non-human creation God seeks and actively promotes *glory*, and for human beings this essentially includes a joyous sense of freedom and worth. Since human life is notably lacking in such glory, and since both human and non-human nature seem to be ravaged by destructive forces which are out of rational control, the theological doctrine of creation is matched by doctrines of sin (or the fall) and of a redemption which will restore glory to all things. These three doctrines taken together attempt to provide a way of understanding why the world fills us with both hope and despair, why we are at once moved by beauty and love and appalled by desolation and degradation. Such doctrines do not really 'explain' anything in an intellectual sense. Rather they articulate a sense of hopefulness against all appearances, based on a belief that there is a God who is neither malevolent nor impotent but is a gentle power for good; and also that this power is available for us to draw on (but is never forced upon us).

How then might such a theological world-view give content to the idea of profession, as a 'calling which leads to a public declaration'? Here I must introduce two additional quasi-religious ideas – gifts and gracefulness. I say 'quasi' because obviously these ideas can be discussed in a non-religious context also. Although 'call' is often thought of as a voice from heaven – in the manner experienced by Paul on the Damascus road, for example – for most people it is more likely to be found in an awareness of possessing gifts. Such gifts may consist of abilities we have inherited and developed or of opportunities which open up before us. A theology of vocation views these abilities or opportunities not as accidents but as evidence of the active intervention in each person's life of a creative and redeeming God. It is left to us to use such gifts productively or to squander or ignore them. To respond with gratitude and imagination to the gifts we have received is to find our specific vocation. This however is not to be seen as a once-for-all event but as a continued state of readiness to respond to the changing opportunities and circumstances of our lives. The notion of a historically involved God (the God present in the milking) entails a dynamic view of vocation.

It is obvious that we often have the greatest difficulty in both finding and responsibly using our natural gifts, and it is here that the idea of grace comes in; or rather, a cluster of related ideas: grace, gratitude and gracefulness. I have already noted how, because of sin, any attempt to describe vocation simply by looking at the created order – at what we are given in ability and opportunity – will be theologically incomplete. Creation is so distorted that God's benevolent purpose for the glory of all things is hard to discern. But grace, the theological term for the redemptive activity of God, mediates a different reality. Grace may be described as God's refusal to accept the ultimacy of failure in any person's life. It is the gentle power I have referred to earlier that persists beyond reasonable expectation to seek good. When people become aware of this grace they have a sense of liberation from the past and an awareness of recovering a lost freedom and dignity. The sense of gratitude which grace brings leads to a revaluation of one's abilities and use of time in order to share what one has received as fully as possible with others. Thus grace leads to gratitude and gratitude leads to *gracefulness* – a spontaneous, unforced care for others which comes from the person who knows what it means to need love and acceptance. In this context all vocation becomes in essence a call to *love*, the use of talents and abilities in service of neighbour. One theologian describes the effect of such graceful love: 'There is nothing more delightful and lovable on earth than one's neighbour. Love does not think about doing works, it finds joy in people.[10]

## Vocation and profession

I am aware that an atmosphere of heady optimism, indeed of unrealistic religious sentimentality, must seem to have infected me at this point. For what has all this talk of graceful loving to do with the phenomena of professional power and privilege discussed earlier?

The connection is to be found in the 'public declaration' aspect of professionalism, especially the declarations of those professions which deal with people at times of heightened vulnerability. Doctors, nurses, social workers, lawyers (in some aspects of their work) and various other 'helping occupations' profess a dedication to the vulnerable beyond mere consideration of financial gain or personal inclination. In my view we must relate these declarations of altruism to the three doctrines of creation, fall and redemption to which I referred earlier.

### Creation and professionalism

Perhaps the most notable feature of contemporary professionalism (compared with notions in previous generations of a class-based or religiously based status) is that it depends upon the qualities of intellect and personality which can be more fully developed by appropriate education. Professionalism may be seen as a balance of theoretical knowledge, skill derived from experience and the ability to form appropriate relationships. Thus the claim to professionalism is not just part of a naked struggle for power; its validity may be tested by seeing whether practitioners are the genuine purveyors of the qualities their public declaration offers or whether their claims are founded upon opportunism and sham. The Creator (as I have noted) gives specific qualities to different individuals, so the concept of vocation should be a revelation of the charlatan. To be professional is to show the ability and willingness to develop one's talents in the service of others.

*Sin (the fall) and professionalism*

The emphasis on vocational aspects of professionalism should not, however, be used to bolster a 'moral superiority' view of the group whose abilities fit them for this task. It is very important to note that there is no particular merit in having specific abilities or characteristics – intelligence, for example, or physical strength or a physical appearance regarded as beautiful. These 'accidents of nature' may be socially valued but their possessor should not be admired for that reason. What is morally admirable or deplorable is the use to which such unmerited abilities are put. Thus the person who has the ability and opportunity to pursue a professional career is to be regarded not as a 'culture hero' but as an unusually favoured person, in the sense that circumstances have made it possible to combine an occupation with the general human vocation to love (that is, to honour and help others). Many occupations do not provide this opportunity and the 'vocation to love' must be found outside or perhaps even in opposition to the occupation. The professional helper is a fortunate person whose service of others is – or rather should be – a response of gratitude for unmerited privilege.

We all know however that the real situation is often far different from this. Professionals feel insufficiently rewarded, insufficiently recognised by society. The mere pursuit of their vocation is not enough reward in a situation where competition for material benefits is the social norm. Feeling under threat, they want the moral status of disinterested helpers *and* the comfortable life-style of the successful trader. This is a natural and no doubt excusable desire in a human society shot through with the fragmenting effects of sin, but it does put the professional helper in an especially exposed position. The betrayal of trust by a professional who seeks only self-advantage is a betrayal both of the self and of the other. Perhaps I might use biblical imagery to illustrate this point. The figures of Judas and Peter represent two different kinds of betrayal: Judas, in the strange inevitability of the passion narrative, has the vocation to betray Jesus – this he does consistently and to the bitter end; Peter claims that he has absolute loyalty, but when 'the chips are down' he denies his affiliation with Jesus to protect himself. It is the part of Peter which we professional helpers tend to play.

*Redemption and professionalism*

This leads me to the third theological doctrine, redemption. It may seem odd to introduce this concept as something relevant to all professionals irrespective of their religious beliefs. Yet I want to suggest that it is relevant in the sense that the acknowledgement that professional care is full of contradiction between egoism and altruism, that it leads to inappropriate use of power for personal gain, that many of the claims to be 'serving humanity' or 'putting patients/clients first', are nothing less than hypocrisy or at best a self-deluding response to the often misguided praise of those we *do* manage to help a little. All this rather painful reappraisal which is being forced upon most professional groups by a new mood of self-criticism can bring a very different kind of reward. The word I used before, and which I must now repeat, is *gracefulness*. By this I mean the spontaneity which comes from those who do not need a status, a power base or an infallibility of knowledge and skill to defend themselves from criticism and failure and to feel that helping others is worth it.

Gracefulness – the gracefulness of the dancer, for example – is a mysterious ability to be under the constraint of our bodily limitation, our clumsy attempt to stand upright, to balance as we move, and yet to let go fearlessly without tension. There is a gracefulness in caring consistently and skilfully for others, and this comes when we acknowledge the ambiguity of our position as those who claim to do good in a world where good and evil are so inextricably bound together.

Edwin Muir says this very well in his poem 'One Foot in Eden'. To show that what I say is in the nature of hints and intuitions rather than of a logically defended case, I will conclude with some lines from this poem:

> Time's handiworks by time are haunted
> And nothing new can separate
> The corn and tares compactly grown.
> The amorial weed in stillness bound
> About the stalk; these are our own.
> Evil and good stand thickly around
> In the fields of charity and sin
> Where we shall lead our harvest in.
>
> But famished field and blackened tree
> Bear fruits in Eden never known,
> Blossoms of grief and charity
> Bloom in these darkened fields alone.
> Which had Eden ever to say
> Of hope and faith and pity and love
> Until was buried all its day
> And memory found its treasure trove?
> Strange blessings never in Paradise
> Fall from these beclouded skies.[11]

In the midst of such ambiguity professionals may indeed rediscover their true vocation.

## Notes

1 Wingram, G. (1957), *Luther on Vocation*. Edinburgh, Oliver & Boyd, p. 9.
2 Becker, H. S. (1962), 'The nature of a profession' in Henry, N. B., ed., *Education for the Professions*. University of Chicago Press.
3 Halmos, P. (1965), *The Faith of the Counsellors*. London, Constable.
4 See, for example, Stevens, B. J. (1979), *Nursing Theory: analysis, application, evaluation*. Boston, Little, Brown; British Association of Social Workers (1977), *The Social Work Task*. London; Butrym, Z. T. (1976), *The Nature of Social Work*. London, Macmillan.
5 Halmos, P. (1970), *The Personal Service Society*. London, Constable.
6 For a full discussion of this aspect of professionalism see Millerson, G. (1964), *The Qualifying Associations: a study in professionalisation*. London, Routledge & Kegan Paul.
7 Wilding, P. (1982), *Professional Power and Social Welfare*. London, Routledge & Kegan Paul, p. 5.
8 Carr-Saunders, A. M. and Wilson, R. A. (1933), *The Professions*. Oxford University Press.
9 Freidson, E. (1970), *Profession of Medicine*. New York, Dodd, Mead.
10 Wingram, op. cit. p. 43.
11 *Collected Poems* (1984). London, Faber.

# 2  Nursing: a paradigm of caring

*Jean McFarlane*

Nursing is classed along with others as a 'caring profession'. By focusing on my own profession I would like to attempt an analysis of some of the elements of caring it portrays and put the question as to whether this in any way represents a paradigm of caring.

## Caring and curing

In the DHSS Report of the Committee on Nursing (1972), Lord Briggs identified nursing and midwifery as 'the major caring profession'. I suggest this was not just because nurses are numerically the largest group of carers in the health service but because the major focus of their work is caring. But rather than helping nurses in clarifying their role, the use of the concept of care or caring actually creates problems both of definition and of conflicting values.

Caring is a woolly concept and notoriously difficult of precise definition. It is first a noun meaning 'trouble, anxiety, serious attention, heed, caution, pains' (*Concise Oxford Dictionary*), but also a verb meaning to 'feel concern or interest, regard, deference, affection, liking'. Although at times all these words may be relevant to nursing they do not define a role or specialised function with any precision. Caring can describe actions which range from the self-care which a healthy person normally exercises for himself, to the care provided by friends and family, and to the highly specialised care provided by professionals. Briggs (DHSS, 1972) acknowledges that 'most nursing in society is carried out within the family by non-professionals - by relatives and friends ...Yet such care must by its nature be limited and will in large numbers of cases be quite inadequate.' He goes on to suggest a way in which professional care is distinguished from lay care:

> Professional nursing and midwifery - that is to say nursing and midwifery for which individuals are selected, educated, managerially deployed and paid - has as its objectives continuity and co-ordination of care in the interests of comfort, recovery and integrity of the person being cared for.

In its most commonly accepted definition the unique role of the nurse (Henderson, 1966) is defined in terms of doing what the individual normally does for himself, that is, activities leading to health, its recovery or a peaceful death. Henderson suggests that three factors may lead to a deficit in the ability to carry out self-care and so validate nursing intervention – lack of strength, will or knowledge.

Because of the lack of scientific precision in the concept of caring, it fails to provide a blueprint for scientifically-based professional action in modern health care and a basis from which the efficiency and effectiveness of such action can be judged. Consequently some believe that it is not in the interests of nursing to continue to use such an imprecise term as 'care' or 'caring' in the attempt to define the role and function of its practitioners. A doctor who served with me on the Royal Commission on the NHS felt strongly that as long as nurses retained this 'sloppy, sentimental' view of their role they would never become a respected profession with a scientific basis for action. In his view the remedy was for nurses to see themselves as doctors' assistants with the exciting vista of contributing to medical science. Roper, a respected author of nursing texts, also rejects the care concept in the analysis of nursing, feeling that it detracts from the meaning of the word 'nursing' itself and the science of nursing which she calls 'nursology'. Even in the lay press there are critics of the imprecision of the term. For example, Kenneth Rose (1982) spoke of the 'tendentious rhetoric' used in an appeal by the Dean of Salisbury when he stressed the need to 'emphasise again the value of the human and personal, the strength of tenderness, the necessity of intuitive sensitivity and compassionate caring'.

Much as these criticisms may be justified, I believe the word *care* and the activity of *caring* hold a common meaning which is understood as an integral part of a number of professions and is a major element in nursing. Part of our resistance may be that the notions of care and caring are affectively oriented and value-laden. However I would argue that the values implicit in these notions are necessary precursors of professional action.

Mauksch (1975) suggests that:

> Patient care in a significant way, is a dramatic interaction, negotiation and encounter between the ideologies of medicine, nursing and other health occupations. These occupations though interdependent and complementary are not alike nor are they linear, certainly they are not given to identical priorities. Furthermore they do not participate in patient care with equal power, equal mandate and equal institutional support.

There is dissonance also between values of care and cure as expressed in goals, beliefs and action, and therefore at times there are conflicts between the ideologies of caring and curing.

Mauksch makes a sociological analysis of the ideologies underlying patient care and their outcomes in terms of power, authority and resource allocation. Within the delivery of patient care he finds differing ideologies which reflect simultaneous consensus and conflict. He writes that 'cure is a more focused legitimising force than the much more broadly conceptualised ideology of care' and suggests that the traditional ideology of cure places primacy on recovery justifying its activities by the requirements of healing and intervention. Care on the other hand focuses more on the needs of the whole human being, his family and situational needs in a broader, supportive and contextually sensitive way. To Mauksch then, cure and care and their ideologies represent different emphases and priorities in patient care and he sees these outlined in the nursing and medical roles respectively. Yet the interdependence of care and cure is demonstrated by Leininger (1974): 'caring acts and decisions make the crucial difference in effective curing consequences. Therefore, it is caring that is the most essential and crucial ingredient to any curative process.'

## Scientific and humanistic values in caring

Mayeroff (1972) uses a philosophical approach to clarifying the concept of caring, analysing its meaning in different contexts and related concepts. He identifies eight essential ingredients of caring which have been summarised by Chinn (1979):

1   KNOWLEDGE is not simply a matter of good intentions or warm regards, but involves explicit and implicit knowing who others are, what their limitations and powers are and most importantly, what would be conducive to their growth.

2   ALTERNATING RHYTHMS between interacting with others, reflecting on the felt consequences of the interaction and maintaining or modifying one's own behaviour based on the effects of the mutual interaction, are another part of caring.

3   PATIENCE does not simply wait for something to happen, but enables others to grow and develop in their own time and style.

4   HONESTY involves an active openness and confrontation with one's self and with the other person. This honesty goes far beyond merely intending not to deceive the other, but sensing other persons as they really are, rather than as we would like them to be. It involves taking other persons seriously and respecting their changing needs without imposing our own desires and needs on them.

5   TRUST means appreciating the independent existence of others, allowing them to grow in their own way.

6   HUMILITY involves continually seeking to learn about others, always being ready and willing to learn about both the other and the self. The caring person is always willing to learn from others regardless of the societal status or 'line of authority' in which they come to an encounter. Caring persons are aware of their own limitations and are able to acknowledge them openly.

7   HOPE is the possibility of something worthy of commitment, mitigating

against despair. Hope in this sense is not wishful thinking or unfounded expectations, but rather it enlarges the significance of the present and calls forth present energies to reach for a realistic future.

8  COURAGE makes possible the taking of risks informed by knowledge of the past and present experience, and is founded in trust in one's own and the other's ability to grow.

The first component of care identified by Mayeroff is 'knowledge'. As he says, good intentions and warm regards are not enough, there is a need for general and specific knowledge. Caring in nursing involves specific knowledge of an individual's needs, his powers and limitations and how to respond to them, which has as its basis a general, scientifically tested body of knowledge of biological and behavioural functioning. This knowledge base of nursing action is supported by *scientific* values with their emphasis on competence and scholarship. The other components of caring (honesty, trust and so on) are more firmly bedded in *moral* or *humanistic* values.

At the centre of the concept of caring there is thus an inherent conflict to which Fry (1981) draws attention, the conflict between scientific and humanistic values. The conflict is probably felt more acutely in nursing, which leans to the humanistic aspect of caring, than in medicine, which places a priority on scientific values. Yet as nursing moves towards an increasingly scientific basis for care, there is a tendency to generalise the approaches used, so that in Carper's (1979) view the individual may be treated increasingly as an object or abstraction, an object of science. The conflict may also be noted by patients, as Menninger (1984) points out:

> The delivery of health care, regardless of how competently the specific tasks are carried out in relation to a given patient or how consistent with the latest scientific knowledge it is, is often perceived by the client as lacking the poignant, personally experienced feeling of being cared for.

In Carper's view the two factors which have contributed most to the erosion of care are specialisation and the development of science and technology.

## Stories of caring

My own thinking about caring in the practice of nursing has been helped forward by identifying caring stories within the Christian tradition, specifically in the parables and miracles of Jesus. I want now to outline briefly some of the ways in which they have helped.

### Hygiene, cleansing and comfort – washing the feet

Washing feet and other acts of hygiene, cleansing and comfort are basic acts of nursing care and there is an interesting reciprocity in the New Testament stories. Jesus washed his disciples' feet, but he also had his feet washed. In this act we see humility enough to become a servant which is part of any caring. In the woman we see a contrast with the Pharisaical host, she used her tears, her hair, her touch, her kisses, that is, *herself* and all her life savings in one profligate act. In that act I see something of what caring in nursing means – a therapeutic use of self. In another relation to another anointing we read, 'The house was filled with the odour.' I believe there is a fragrance to caring acts that is beyond their scientific validity.

*The feeding of the five thousand*
It may be surprising that I classify the feeding of the five thousand as a caring miracle. I have looked at incidents that illustrate 'caring' in my own professional practice and feeding and nurturing is central to nursing. There is an interesting exhortation to identify what resources we have: 'What have you got? Go and see', and a recognition of their inadequacy; five loaves for five thousand, that is very reminiscent of nursing.

These are examples of caring acts to meet very physical and down to earth needs for food and cleanliness. They are however invested with spiritual meaning. The feeding of the five thousand becomes a parable of spiritual feeding and spiritual life; the washing of the feet quickly passes to the need for spiritual cleansing.

The incidents I have chosen seem to have an exemplary aspect: 'Go and do likewise'; 'You give them to eat'; 'If I have washed your feet you ought to wash one another's feet.' It is almost as though we need constantly to have caring acts held up before us and be told 'now you do it', so that they become the fabric of life and transform the commonplace.

**The good Samaritan – a paradigm for caring?**
A further caring story, that of the good Samaritan, has become a central focus of what I see as a paradigm of caring. There is a very explicit statement about caring in the story: 'He cared for him.' The parable portrays how to love one's neighbour by caring. The Greek word for care in the parable is *epimeliomai*. The root of this word means 'it matters to me'. Care 'covers' the person with the knowledge that they matter to us. There are four elements in the parable to which I wish to draw attention; these relate to need, motivation, action and outcome.

1   Need: for economic resources – the victim in the parable had been robbed; for wounds to be dressed – the man was injured; for physical help – he was unable to help himself (he was half dead).
2   Motivation: significantly the professionals (the priest and the

Levite) lacked this – they passed by on the other side; the Samaritan came to where the man was in need and had compassion on him. His caring action was motivated by compassion. 'He *cared* for him.'
3   Action: a variety of significant actions are demonstrated – binding up wounds; provision of transport; provision of accommodation; financial provision. The Samaritan provided practical care at a cost to himself by giving up his own ass. His care was given irrespective of race or religion.
4   Outcome: aftercare or follow-up. Ongoing care was offered. 'Whatsoever is more I will repay thee.'

I think the parable of the good Samaritan could become a paradigm for caring. Let me look at the four elements I have outlined as these are to be seen in nursing.

### Need
One of the great problems in providing care is that needs are specialised and regarded as the province of specialised workers. For example, we identify social, medical, nursing needs and provide specialised social, medical and nursing care. Yet needs are intimately related, hence the related welfare legislation of the 1940s and the ongoing problems for autonomous professions in reaching concensus in multidisciplinary teams, and the problems of team leadership.

The problems we face with ethical implications are:

1   How is need defined?
2   Who defines need?
3   The stereotyping of need and the routinisation of care.

Bradshaw (1972) identifies four separate definitions of need used in the personal social services which are I believe applicable to other caring services:

1   Normative need – what the expert or professional defines as need in any given situation.
2   Felt need – equated with want as perceived by the individual.
3   Expressed need or demand.
4   Comparative need. By this definition a measure of need is found by studying the characteristics of those in receipt of a service.

In considering the need for nursing care it is important to focus on the individual in need. I believe the ideal, the 'ought' of nursing is a professional relationship between nurses and their patients or clients in which, while the nurse brings to the situation professional knowledge and skills in helping individuals with activities they normally do for themselves, the activities remain primarily the province of the individual and still ideally under their management. The relationship is one in which the patient has superior knowledge of how he normally manages his own self-care. The nurse adapts her knowledge and skill so that such functions are maintained as nearly as possible to what is normal for that individual. Henderson sees the nurse very much in this substitutionary or surrogate role when she says somewhat dramatically:

> She is temporarily the consciousness of the unconscious, the love of life for the suicidal, the leg of the amputee, the eyes of the newly blind, a means of locomotion for the infant, the 'mouthpiece' of those too weak or withdrawn to speak ...

and so on. The reality of nursing is different. We have stereotyped need and routinised the care given so that often we give 'standard' care for routine health situations irrespective of individual need.

*Motivation to care*

The Samaritan was motivated by compassion – 'feeling with'. Our intense preoccupation with a scientific basis for health care tends to have led us to neglect the all-important springs of human action. It is to be regretted that in our action-oriented approach to the urgent demands of acute health care we neglect to analyse the values and ideologies which motivate and underpin our actions.

Although the meaning of the term 'value' as used in the social sciences and philosophy is by no means clear (Macmillan and Kneller, 1964), at a simple level the definition given by Rath *et al.* (1966) is serviceable. Their definition is 'those elements that show how a person has decided to use his life' or 'general guides to behaviour'. Values operate in very complex circumstances (like health care) and usually involve more than simple extremes of right and wrong, good or bad, true or false; typically they involve conflicting demands and complicated judgments. Like Leininger (1974) I recognise a challenge to re-establish and reaffirm human values in health care.

Nursing has traditionally been nurtured in an ideology of vocationalism. Williams (1974) describes the ideology of vocation as an aid to psychological adjustment to the sick adult's helplessness. The hemiplegic, for example, whose care entails 'washing, feeding and cleaning away bodily excretions – tasks that an adult normally performs in the independence and privacy that partly define him as an adult in the first place': the task may be repugnant to both nurse and patient and an assault on the adult male status when being cared for by an adult female. Caring for the helpless thus violates the normal relationships between adult men and women in our society. Williams maintains that to deal with this situation as an act of sacrifice, as a vocation, retrieves the status of the nurse and the status of the adult for whom they are performed. To be 'called' to such work and to perform it sacrificially is to sanctify and consecrate both task and person. She contrasts this with the professional ideology in which the hemiplegic is conceptualised and categorised as hemiplegic, aphasic, incontinent and manifesting a degree of circulatory collapse to which the nurse brings scientific methods of care. The ideology, whether it be humanistic, vocational, professional or occupational, affects both the conceptualisation of the task and the relationship of nurse and patient. However I believe these four ideologies are by no means mutually exclusive.

It seems to me that the word 'love', if it can be rehabilitated, expresses most aptly the basic motivational force for caring. True, we may need to analyse along with C. S. Lewis even that word. In nursing one may have genuine affection for some patients, experience friendship with a few, even recognise Eros as present at times. However it is the love as seen in 'charitas' or 'agape' which most effectively motivates the action of caring. This emotion has to be translated into acts of relationship and physical care in nursing. Agape takes up and uses the whole person's, strength and mind and reaches out to others. Caring acts are an expression of that love.

*Action – nursing care*
The action of giving nursing care is a process. The same decision-making process underlies care giving by any profession. There is assessment of needs for care following data collection, objectives for care are set and a plan of care is drawn up. This plan incorporates a specification of the kind of acts needed to meet the care objectives, that is, the *what* of care. In addition the *how* and the *who* of care are specified. The plan is then implemented and subsequently evaluated. In nursing we call this decision-making process 'the nursing process'. In essence it has four stages:

1  assessment
2  planning
3  implementation
4  evaluation

The same decision-making process is exemplified in the medical decision-making process underlying diagnosis and prescription of treatment to which the nursing process is complementary.

More relevant to this discussion is the nature of decision-making between nurse and patient. Nursing is essentially an interactive process having supportive and substitutionary goals. It is basic to this position that the patient is involved in information-giving about self-care methods in health and in decision-making about goals and methods of care and their evaluation. Underlying such an approach is a value system and ideology about the nature and worth of man as an individual human being with psychosocial needs interrelated with physical needs, and the skills of human relations.

Yet a plan of care is often promulgated which denies these beliefs. Frequently there is variance between the ideology of the nursing education system with its humanistic value system and the practice of nursing cast in a mass-production industrial mould. The patient is often seen as a series of tasks rather than as an integrated person with human needs. The ward sister manages the ward by task-detailing rather than patient assignment. The ideology of nursing care is often at variance with its practice, and those being initiated are bewildered and in conflict with the real situation of nursing as it is rather than as it ought to be.

A better way of resolving this conflict lies, I believe, in a number of different directions:

1   Adequate preparation of the ward sister for her crucial role including values clarification.
2   Development of clinical roles.
3   Synthesis of practice and teaching posts to overcome the conflict in ideologies, that is, a review of nursing education.
4   A review of manpower resources for the reality of individualised care.

A number of studies in the Department of Nursing at Manchester University and other places demonstrate how inadequately nursing care organisation subserves the stated humanistic aims of nursing. Pembrey (1980) shows how inadequately the ward sister carries out the management function of assessing patient needs on an individualised basis. Grypdonck *et al.* (1979) report a base-line study in which piecemeal and inadequate approaches to care are illustrated. Interestingly Miller (1980) sets out to identify long-stay hospital wards where patient-oriented practice was carried out but has found in most situations that the method of work organisation was not consistent from shift to shift or day to day. However she found that there were marked differences in patient outcomes where systematic decision-making about care (the nursing process) was used. Work by Metcalfe (1982) calls into question many of our value assumptions about nursing care organisation. In a piece of action research she found greater job satisfaction for nurses in patient allocation; the patients themselves found little difference.

*Outcome*
Part of the professional process of caring involves evaluation by outcomes. As in planning patient care, patient evaluation of nursing

care is essential but only a part of a larger quality control programme which would include audits of care, case reviews and so on. These may result in a restatement of objectives. But the outcomes of care are not nearly so unidirectional nor capable of complete success as the outcomes of cure. Complete care or complete success in care may be indefinable and unattainable since its objects are support and substitution. In nursing care the greatest skill, the greatest success, may be in helping someone to find meaning in illness or to achieve a peaceful death according to his own faith – yet it is interesting that if one analyses nursing care plans with this expressed objective one may find activities more compatible with 'cure' and life promotion. The moral dilemmas of terminal care are perhaps greater for the nurse than the doctor. The doctor reaches the point of saying, 'there is nothing more that we can do'. The nurse sustains in that situation but must decide how actively, which life systems and for how long.

## Conclusion

To be a caring profession means many things. It means a discipline of mind in researching and developing a body of knowledge for practice; it entails recognition of the economic and political nature of caring services. This chapter focuses attention on the nature of the caring professions by examining the role and function and the aspirations of nursing. For many years nursing has been practised with routinised approaches to tasks rather than the holistic care of individuals with physical, psychological and spiritual care integrated. But there is also a spiritual significance in caring; I suggest that if this is neglected, then the nature of caring is eroded.

In searching for a paradigm of caring, nursing has been analysed in terms of the definition of need, the motivation to care, caring action and the outcome of care. These elements could be demonstrated in other caring professions. Between the different caring professions there are shared dilemmas regarding the nature of need, the decision-making process, professional ideologies, professional relationships with clients and the organisation of care. Within nursing there are dilemmas of value orientations and ideologies and their compatibility with nursing as practised in educational and management contexts. Between caring professions there are conflicts in respect of ideologies and goals and means, which may not be shared even though the professionals must act collaboratively in care. It is to such dilemmas that we must constantly address ourselves.

# References

Bradshaw, J. (1972), 'The concept of social need' in Gilbert, N. and Specht, N., eds, *Planning and Social Welfare Issues, Models and Tasks*. NJ, Prentice-Hall.

Carper, B. A. (1979). 'The ethics of caring', *Advanced Nursing Studies*, 1, 3, pp. 11–19.

Chinn, P. (1979), 'Issues in lowering infant mortality: a call for ethical action', *Advanced Nursing Studies*, 1, 3, pp. 68–9.

DHSS (1972), *Report of the Committee on Nursing*, chairman Lord Briggs. Cmnd. 5115. London, HMSO.

Fry, S. A. (1981). 'Accountability in research: the relationship in scientific and humanistic values', *Advances in Nursing Sciences*, 4, 1.

Grypdonck, M., Koene, M., Windy, T. and Blanpan, J. C. (1979), 'Integrating nursing: a holistic approach to the delivery of nursing care', *International Journal of Nursing Studies*, January.

Henderson, V. (1966), *The Nature of Nursing*. London, Collier Macmillan.

Leininger, M. (1974), *Humanism, Health and Cultural Values in Health Care*. Phila., Davis.

Macmillan, C. J. B. and Kneller, G. F. (1964), 'Philosophy of education', *Review of Educational Research*, xxxiv, 1, February.

Mauksch, H. (1975), 'Ideology, interaction and patient care in hospitals', *Social Science and Medicine*, vol. 7.

Mayeroff, M. (1972), *On Caring*. New York, Harper Row.

Menninger, W. W. (1984), 'Caring as part of health care quality', *Journal of the American Medical Association*. 8, pp. 886–7.

Metcalfe, C. A. (1982), 'Applying organisational theory to the management of nursing care'. Unpublished PhD thesis, University of Manchester.

Miller, A. (1980), 'A study of work organisation by nurses related to patient outcomes in long-stay hospital wards'. Unpublished interim report.

Pembrey, S. (1980), *The Ward Sister – Key to Nursing: a study of the organisation of individualised nursing*. London, RCN.

Rath, L., Hamin, M. and Simon, S. (1966), *Values and Nursing*. Columbus, Merrill.

Rose, K. (1982), *Sunday Telegraph*, 29 August.

Williams, K. (1974), 'Ideologies of nursing: their meanings and implications', *Nursing Times Occasional Papers*, 8 August.

# 3 On the concept of nursing care

*Alison Kitson*

The comments of a general practitioner, Dr Vernon Coleman (1985), attracted some attention in the popular press when he claimed that if nurses were to discard the more traditional uniform of white hats and starched aprons and wear short skirts and black stockings, they could make patients feel much better. Undeterred by this archaic, outmoded imagery, the good doctor went on to say: 'the sight of a pretty nurse dressed like that would make any man's heart miss a beat or two and make him feel happier or cheerful'. The justification for such a comment was the medically proven fact that cheerful people get better quicker. As a conciliatory gesture – or an afterthought – he then suggested that hairdressers and beauticians could be employed on female wards to evoke a similar sort of well-being to that manufactured by the pretty nurses on the male patients.

Despite its rather flippant and tactless nature, the point Dr Coleman was attempting to make is, I believe, a valid one. He was simply suggesting that patients have to feel better as well as get better. On a more serious – and acceptable – level he went on to suggest that if hospitals were more colourful, cheerful and pleasant places to be sick in, then patients would feel better more quickly and hence I presume get better at a quicker rate. That Dr Coleman viewed the nurse as an integral part of the process of helping patients feel better was all too obvious.

The question is whether it is part of the nurse's job to make patients feel better. Leaving the sexual stereotypes aside, I want to consider what it means for someone who is ill to experience 'feeling better'. I should like to illustrate what I mean by sharing three experiences of my own which relate to ill health, nursing intervention and the outcome – either feeling better, or not feeling better. Each of the experiences was significant in that I learned something about caring and about nursing.

The first incident was commonplace. I was ten years of age and next in line for a routine school eyesight test. While I had known for some time that my eyesight was poor, I had not disclosed this fact to anyone for fear of the dreaded NHS spectacles. I can still remember the school nurse's reaction to my tears of anguish. She put a large fleshy arm round my shoulders and drew me close to her when I began to cry. What was important was that she did not make me feel ashamed or embarrassed for reacting in the way I did and in fact demonstrated by her words and embrace that she understood. She had made me feel better and I was able to face the doctor and the NHS spectacles with much more aplomb.

The second experience was quite different, and several years later. I had already started my nursing training and found myself again the recipient of medical treatment. This time the problem was more difficult to locate than a simple case of myopia. After a series of medical investigations and examinations still no firm diagnosis had been reached. For me this was a time of acute anguish and worry, an experience no doubt common to many individuals who find themselves at odds with their body and consequently propelled into a world of investigations, reports, hospital beds and wakeful nights. During this time I experienced something of the feeling of utter isolation and despair which is part of physical illness. No one else would go through this; it was my body which was giving trouble, it was my future in jeopardy. While I craved comfort and support from colleagues and friends I could not at any time say that I was helped to feel better. This time feeling better came with recovery.

Connected to these events was my reaction to a nursing situation some months later. I was working in a long-term geriatric ward looking after a group of elderly ladies who had been there for a long time. One woman in fact had been in hospital for twenty-seven years. Her body, because of the years of disuse, was like a jelly. It wobbled and fell on to the sheets when one attempted to move her. She was semi-conscious, incontinent, totally dependent on nursing staff. While I continued to provide nursing care – feeding, washing, removing excreta – I experienced a profound sense of having failed this person, of not having been able to communicate in a way that I, as a person, should be communicating to another human being. On the surface it seemed as if I was fulfilling my duty – I was caring – but was I really caring for this patient or any of the others in the ward? Did I know anything of how they felt? Could I know? Had I made any of them feel better?

All of which brings me back to my original question: has nursing anything to do with making people feel better? In order to elucidate this concept as it relates to nursing I want to distinguish between the notions of 'feeling better' and 'getting better', proposing that the former is the legitimate domain of the nurse while the latter is the focus of medical care. In comparing and contrasting feeling and getting better, I want to put forward the idea that while it is the implicit belief, or more realistically the hope, of patients that nurses work towards making them feel better, the profession's own perspective is more closely linked to the medical goal of 'getting better'. The result is that the emotional and affective dimensions of nursing care are subjugated to the acquired nursing goal of helping patients to get better. Patients in the main are left to cope in whatever way they can with their feelings.

## Feeling better

It is part of our being human that our senses react pleasurably to certain stimuli, that we can experience a sense of well-being or pleasure when we see or hear or smell or taste something we like. Such experiences are heightened when they are juxtaposed with that which was uncomfortable, painful and distressing. A warm bath is all the more pleasurable when it comes after a frustrating, cold, miserable day. Illness is one experience in life where there is an assault not only on our sensibilities, on our capacity to take pleasure out of life, but on our very existence. Illness affects what we can do; it affects how we feel, it frightens us; we may feel vulnerable, lonely, isolated. It is at such times that we also realise how inextricably mixed our body and soul are. To be a creature then is to be linked to a body in such a total way that all descriptions of self apart from the body are mere abstractions (Campbell, 1984, p. 96). And as the body *is* through the senses, then to feel, to suffer, to gain pleasure, to laugh, to cry, are of the body. Treating someone who is ill then requires not only the identification and treatment of the cause of the illness – whether it be an invading micro-organism, a genetic aberration or a psychological upset – but also a reconstitution of the sensibilities, of the emotions.

Most of us are familiar with the medical protocol related to getting better – it involves entrusting oneself to the skill and competence of a doctor and complying with a course of treatment. The treatment regimen may be painful, nauseating, demanding, exhausting, but despite the discomfort one subjects oneself to it because of the future goal, to get better, to recover. Implicit in that medical goal, the hope of recovery, is the belief that by getting better one will also feel better. In other words the repaired body will automatically lead to a repaired sensibility, a regaining of one's ability to enjoy life.

It may be useful to consider whether these two notions relate as closely as one supposes. If feeling better is a function of getting better, then for those people who have to contend with incurable illnesses the future would indeed be grave. The hospice movement has helped to highlight the difference between the notions of feeling and getting better, demonstrating in its activities that when the goal of getting better is no longer a reality one can still work towards the equally important goal of helping the person feel better. For someone whose body is wracked with pain, cahexic, his resolve and determination perhaps bruised and forlorn, who knows that he will never get better, what is there to do but to hope that today's pain will be more tolerable, that somehow those sensations, experiences, even daydreams which evoke a sense of well-being, of wholeness, can be caught up into the body to make it feel better. To help someone feel better is surely a distinctive challenge, separate from yet complementary to the medical goal, and which requires closeness, tenderness, dialogue and contact.

Unlike the protocol which has been established to help the patient know what to expect from the doctor and how to cooperate in the process of getting better, the ordinary person is not given the same sort of guidance in working out who it is or what it is that helps him feel better. The sick person in hospital may harbour some old-fashioned notion that it is the nurse who will be meeting this ill-defined and not-to-be-readily-mentioned set of problems. Uncomfortable hospital buildings, archaic routines, officious personnel are all more or less accepted as an inevitable consequence of illness. Like the foul-tasting medicine, if it is awful it must be making you better. Yet underneath, the patient, the person, does look for reassurance, contact, warmth, and again either consciously or subconsciously is looking to the nurse to provide this.

Recognising and responding to this need in the patient has been problematic in a nursing service which has failed to see the provision of a sensitive and caring service as its primary objective. While it has always acknowledged the importance of 'reassuring the patient' and 'caring', the profession has on the whole failed to spell out what this means to patients and what it means to nurses in terms of how they act. Instead nursing has searched for its identity and provided the patient with a set of expectations through emulating and adopting the explicit medical goal of helping patients get better. The result is that ostensibly patients are not being helped to rally the necessary internal forces to enable them to cope with the fear, anguish and frustration of illness; while the nursing profession itself is split between its poorly understood and poorly articulated commitment to care and its more strident resolve to provide individualised deliberative patient-care, the goal of which is to optimise independence and promote recovery. Thus, whereas the sick person has some idea of what the doctors will do to him, he may have greater difficulty articulating just what it is that the nurse is attempting to do.

What evidence is there to support this notion that the profession has denied its expressive role and has concentrated on its instrumental role? In considering what the patient valued most from the nurse, both Anderson (1972) and MacGuire (1969) found that the provision of emotional support was viewed as the most important service. When questioned nurses felt providing emotional support and basic nursing care were the most important parts of their job, while doctors believed that the safe execution of medical orders was a priority. Despite the fact that nurses identified the provision of emotional support as an integral part of their job, a large number of research findings show that in the outworking of what is seen to be an important concept the nursing profession is much less united. Studies by Wells (1980) and Baker (1978) looking at geriatric nursing have identified a depersonalised routine-centred approach to patient care, where the goal of getting through the work was overriding and notions such as emotional support, patient dignity and helping patients feel better were perceived more as extravagant ideals, not to be contemplated in the real world. Both Baker and Wells talk of the gulf between the reality of nursing and what they perceive as the ideals of providing a personal, dignified, caring service. In denying the expressive dimension of the nurse's caring role, physical care of elderly patients becomes routine, undignified and at times unintentionally cruel. Such observations lead the researchers to question the underlying motives of nurses entering the profession, and to consider the educational context and socialisation process.

What happens when someone decides to become a nurse? What has emerged from investigations is the seemingly inherent conflict between the reactions of a lay person to a situation and those of a trained nurse. Griffen (1983) states that to care for another person is a facility common to our human nature, the ill person's predicament evoking in us a desire to help in that we are responding to our awareness of our own vulnerability. To care also requires an understanding of the other person's situation and particularly his emotional life, his wants, desires, priorities; features normally accommodated in the more personal situation of caring for a loved one, a relative, a friend. I believe this dimension of caring is overlooked in the majority of nurses' training. The affective and emotional aspects of caring for another person are subjugated in favour of learning how to; knowing what to do. Melia (1983) has described nurse training as a desensitising process where those situations which would normally have evoked a response, for example a patient's particular and repeated request for help or the indignity of 'toilet rounds', are after training often overlooked. All the time it would seem that it is the instrumental, action-related role which is set up as the preferred mode of action, the paradox being that the nurse, when questioned, will say that communicating with patients and providing emotional support are of primary importance.

Yet the evidence suggests that nurses engage in behaviour which avoids emotionally conflicting situations, for example Flaskerud *et al.* (1979), Menzies (1960). Nurses would seem to detach themselves from anxiety-provoking situations and continue to tolerate work systems which effectively detach them still further from close and intimate contact with patients. Menzies has attributed this behaviour to nursing's and the nurse's failure to come to terms with the opposing forces of the libido and the destructive elements of the personality. While the overt Freudian explanation of nurses' behaviour is less than convincing, one still has to acknowledge that those features which Menzies describes within the system of nursing – depersonalisation, categorisation, detachment and denial of feelings, and the ritualisation of tasks – do indeed exist; and their very existence must cause one to ask why.

My own interpretation of why such confusion continues in the minds of nurses as to what they do and how they should do it, is not because nurses get pleasure out of deliberately inflicting pain and anguish on patients or that they have been misled or forced into accepting a medical-dominated method of operation; rather I believe that the confusion which affects the nursing profession in its thinking and its service is related to the domination of rational, objective, technological modes of thought over the emotional, subjective, more personal expression of life. Nursing care seems to have fallen foul of a philosophical debate, namely the juxtaposition in life of the rational with the sensual.

Rationality has been traditionally associated with maleness while that which is sensual has been related to femaleness. In the ancient world the female character was seen as inferior to the quest for the single standard of perfection which was male and rational (Lloyd, 1984, p. 75). Descartes claimed that right reasoning involved a struggle away from the sensuous and a complete detachment from the complexity and particularities of ordinary living. This radical separation of mind and body led to a separation of the kind of thought which yields certainty from the more practical concerns of life. The pursuit of such knowledge was seen as the highest form of thought which required a complete transcending of the sensuous. This securing of the foundations of knowledge was seen as a separate activity from the much more relaxed pursuits of everyday life, where mind must accept its intermingling with the body. Lloyd emphasises that although Descartes's method with its new emphasis on the privacy of the mind's natural operations promised to make knowledge accessible to all, even women, his emphasis on the quest for a distinctive kind of reason, that is, a highly abstract mode of thought separable in principle from the emotional complexities and practical demands of ordinary life, led to an even more radical separation.

Tournier (1978) identifies the Renaissance period and in particular the impact of Descartes's ideas as being responsible for the orientation of western society towards what he calls masculine values – power, reason, technology, mastery of machines, gadgets – while what was quintessentially female was banished to the private life, the emotional and affective life, the life of sensitivities, feelings.

In considering the development of medical knowledge and practice from the nineteenth century onwards, one could without a great deal of effort relate its success to the rational, objective, scientific mode of thought. In contrast the development of nursing from a private domestic service into an organised social activity was fraught with all sorts of difficulties. How could a service which was effectively personal, affective in nature, be accommodated into the male-dominated world of machines and systems? I believe two reactions were evoked: one from the medical profession and society at large; the other at a later stage coming from the nursing profession itself.

Nursing was accommodated into the world of medical care by having conferred upon it the image of a service which was on the one hand essentially related to the private domain, to the sensitivities and subjectivity of women, and on the other hand legitimised by nature of its dependent relationship on medical care. The use of sexual stereotypes such as the nurse as mother surrogate or ministering angel conveyed to the public the image of the nurse as the epitome of all that was good and noble about womanhood, again the implicit assumption being that to be a nurse required a certain moral integrity, a certain dedication. At the same time the nurse's position in the outside world was legitimised by manufacturing the complementary image of the nurse as the handmaiden to the doctor. Thus the dilemma of having to accommodate a personal service into a rational objective world was solved by idealising (or stereotyping) the interpersonal skills of caring and by concentrating upon and making more explicit those skills related to the medical goals of care. In this way nursing could be contained within a system which emphasised the objective and rational over the personal and subjective.

Nursing's own interpretation of and reaction to the situation has been more complex, as I believe it has been responding to two distinct influences. The first is the covert or overt influence on nursing to accept as more important that which is rational and objective over the subjective. The second is nursing's desire to avoid sexual stereotyping and what it perceives to be the domination of the medical model of care. However it seems that in its attempt to shed the mother-surrogate image nursing has also denied many of the personal dimensions of its role. Instead it has chosen to concentrate on making nursing more rational, more logical, more objective, in the belief that professional credibility lies in these types of action. Yet without the personal, subjective, emotional dimension the service the nurse provides cannot be called caring. Nursing's failure to achieve the required balance between the necessary objectivity and scientific rigour required to run a service and the personal touch is reflected in the models and theories it uses to explain nursing.

While reacting against the system which relegated it to the status of handmaiden to the doctor, nursing has tried to develop for itself a body of knowledge and mode of operation independent yet complementary to medicine. However, caught up in its attempt to prove its 'coming of age', nurse theorists and academics have devised theories of nursing which deny the essential component – that of care. Having discarded the disease-oriented model of medicine in favour of a person-centred model, nursing embarked on a mission of organising, systematising, rationalising and objectifying nursing actions. The results on the whole have been disappointing. For the most part the disease model has been replaced by an equally 'impersonal' set of concepts, whether it be Johnson's behavioural model (1974), Roy's adaptation model (1970) or Henderson's fourteen basic needs model (1969). While the above theories seek to describe what nurses do, none of them considers the affective relationship between the patient and the nurse. For example, Johnson (1968, p. 4) describes the process of nursing as:

> The temporary imposition of external regulation and control mechanisms, such as inhibiting ineffective behavioural responses, and assisting the patient to acquire new responses. The force also operates by making available those conditions and resources which are essential to fulfilling the functional requirements of the system.

Is this nursing?

Similarly Roy's system of nursing concentrates on the patient's – or, in her terminology, the bio-psycho-social being's – ability to adapt. The nurse focuses her intervention on the stimuli which are inhibiting adaptation by increasing the intensity. Is this nursing? While Henderson's thoughts about nursing are more comprehensible she still tends to describe what the nurse does in a purely functional, mechanistic way, that is, the nurse makes good the patient's deficit in certain self-care areas, the aim being to promote independence.

No doubt there is an implicit assumption running through each of the above theories that the nurse as a person will react and relate to the patient as a person. Nothing is said however about the boundaries, dimensions, expectations or commitments which develop in the relationship. This mechanistic way of thinking has also been encouraged by the widespread use of 'the nursing process', a systematic way of identifying nursing problems and delivering care, which, without the counter-balance of a sensitive awareness of the patient as a person, becomes no more than an objective measure of the nurse's work performance. If nursing care, like medical diagnosis and treatment, can be measured by outcomes, then such a technique is perfectly valid, but if nursing is about how people feel, how they are reacting here and now to a situation, then theories which focus solely on behaviour or adaptive responses and a mechanistic approach do not capture the essence of the tasks.

It is important to stress that nursing is not alone in its failure to link what is essentially an emotional and subjective dimension into a systematic and logical framework. A similar problem exists in such specialities as psychiatry, geriatrics, social work, where a humane and caring approach has had to compete with the more accepted so-called scientific approach to care.

A product of the nursing profession's emphasis on the scientific has been the mastery of techniques over the importance of the personal touch. Henderson (1980) describes an incident which illustrates this tension between humane and technical aspects of nursing. She had gone to visit a friend in an Intensive Care Unit, which she described as large and cold and filled with forbidding monitoring equipment. She found her friend cold, frightened and alone, and on asking him why he had not asked one of the nurses for a blanket he replied that they were too busy. Henderson comments that after less than twelve hours in this high-tech environment even the patients were discounting the importance of simple human fear and discomfort as factors in recovery. For their part the nurses thought they were doing their job by performing various technical procedures, yet had failed to see as their concern the provision of simple comforts such as heat and personal contact.

The over-emphasis of technique at the expense of the personal contact can also be seen in the way quite simple activities have been transformed at times into incomprehensible procedures. Consider for example the bed bath. At one level the washing of one person by another can be a purely mechanical act, the object to clean the integument of potentially harmful micro-organisms, to avoid body odour or to help someone feel more calm, more relaxed, less pained to counter the sense of bodily assault caused by a surgeon's knife.

It appears that there is a deep-seated and fundamental weakness in the way in which nurses have thought and think about what they do and what they value about what they do. Theory and practice are at odds, reality and the ideal do not merge, it seems that the student nurse forfeits her sensitivity, perhaps even her compassion, when she becomes a professional. The goal of getting the body better would seem to have taken precedence over any claims the person might have in wanting or expecting to be helped to feel better.

Getting better is perceived to offer more in the long term, it is a guarantee for future happiness, is it not? Yet it is possible to get better, that is, to be clinically, chemically and biologically sound, but still be utterly miserable, to feel terrible or awful, to feel that one's quality of life has disappeared. To overlook a person's feelings about their illness may not only retard the healing process but may actually prevent it. An example of the importance of feelings was given by a thirty-six year old woman suffering from cancer. Dr Vicky Clement-Jones (1985) said that what annoyed her most about cancer was the lack of detailed practical guidance about treatments she was undergoing and the side-effects of them. She describes her emotional reaction to losing her hair during courses of chemotherapy, the anguish she felt on waking each morning to see her pillow covered in her hair. She felt much better when she hit on the idea of wearing a hair-net, which would catch the hair and which she could shake out each morning. The anguish therefore was not solely because she was losing her hair but had more to do with the disturbing sight of it lying on the pillow. Wearing a hair-net did not stop the process but it helped Vicky cope with it; it helped her to feel better about it all.

Feeling better and getting better are distinct yet complementary goals. The difficulty is that the goal of helping patients feel better has been subsumed into that of getting better. The belief has grown up that if the goal of getting someone better is enthusiastically pursued, then feeling better will follow. My argument is that this is an unfounded assumption, that feeling better is something which has to be worked at right from the start of the illness, that it cannot be considered as the ultimate goal, like cure, but is based in the here and now. I also contend that this is the domain of the nurse. She should know how to make ill people feel better. This requires not only a sensitivity to emotional reactions to illness but also an eminently practical approach to dealing with the results of illness. The nurse through her close physical contact with patients has the ability to encourage a feeling of relaxation, rest, comfort, or she can cause pain or provoke anguish in a variety of ways. Helping another person feel better presupposes a knowledge and acceptance of them as an individual – care therefore is not conceptualised as having anything to do with reacting to a bio-psycho-social being but as helping another person. Such care requires skill in maintaining the delicate balance between the other person's feelings and one's own. It is not a soppy sort of sentimentality but the generation of warmth, understanding, a communication which can be maintained through a range of physical actions performed by the nurse with and for the patient. Nursing is about knowing how to make someone else more comfortable, instilling in another person that sense of being 'on top of it' even in threatening situations, and encouraging a sense of endurance.

It is my belief that the nursing profession is shackled by the pervading trend to value technology and science above the sensitivities and feelings of the individual. This has perpetuated the devaluing of caring in society as graphically evidenced by the constant tension between the allocation of resources to acute and chronic sectors of health care. Nursing has also been caught in the sexual stereotypes used to explain it and more recently is becoming entangled in theories and models which do not reflect that which is essential in nursing. Thus, rather than emulate the medical goal of getting the patient better, nursing ought to focus on caring for the person who is sick and helping him to feel better. Change in nursing thought has to be in this direction, for to see change only in terms of nurses assuming a function like a doctor will do no more than confirm the prejudice of medical superiority, since it will make medical thought and objectivity the model. It is as if the nursing profession, pleased at the idea of having penetrated the world of objectivity and science, remains incapable of the extra effort of imagination needed in order to endow patient care with its own particular and personal character, which is the quality it lacks. It appears that we do not know how to care nor do we think that helping people feel better is as important as getting them better.

## References

Anderson, E. (1972), *The Role of the Nurse*. London, RCN.

Baker, D. E. (1978), 'Attitudes of nurses to the care of the elderly'. Unpublished PhD thesis, University of Manchester.

Campbell, A. V. (1984), *Moderated Love: a theology of professional care*. London, SPCK.

Clement-Jones, V. (1985), in *Sunday Times*, 1 September.

Coleman, V. (1985), reported in *Sun*, 19 August; and *Daily Telegraph*, 19 August.

Flaskerud, J. H., Halloran, E. J., Janken, J., Lund, M. and Zetterlund, J. (1979), 'Avoidance and distancing: a descriptive view of nursing', *Nursing Forum*, 18, 2, pp. 158-74.

Griffen, A. (1983), 'A philosophical analysis of caring in nursing', *Journal of Advanced Nursing*, 8, pp. 289-95.

Henderson, V. (1969), *Basic Principles of Nursing Care*. Geneva, International Council of Nurses.

Henderson, V. (1980), 'Preserving the essence of nursing in a technological age', *Journal of Advanced Nursing*, 5, pp. 245-60.

Johnson, D. E. (1968), 'One conceptual model of nursing'. Paper presented at Vanderbilt University, Nashville (25 April, p. 4).

Johnson, D. E. (1974), 'The behavioural system model for nursing' in Riehl, J. P. and Roy, C., eds, *Conceptual Models for Nursing Practice*. New York, Appleton-Century Crofts.

Lloyd, G. (1984), *The Man of Reason: male and female in western philosophy*. London, Methuen.

MacGuire, J. (1969), *Threshold of Nursing*. London, Bell.

Melia, K. (1983), 'Becoming and being a nurse' in Thompson, Melia and Boyd, *Nursing Ethics*, Edinburgh, Churchill Livingstone.

Menzies, I. (1960), *A Case Study in the Functioning of Social Systems as a Defence Against Anxiety*. London, Tavistock.

Roy, C. (1970), 'Adaptation: a conceptual framework for nursing', *Nursing Outlook*, 18, 3, pp. 42-5.

Tournier, P. (1978), *The Gift of Feeling*. London, SPCK.

Wells, T. (1980), *Problems in Geriatric Nursing Care: a study of nurses' problems in care of old people in hospitals*. Edinburgh, Churchill Livingstone.

# 4 On not caring about the individual

*Bob Brecher*

Over the last decade or so it has become something of a commonplace that doctors, nurses, counsellors and social workers have – among other duties – a particular duty to the individual or client with whom they are dealing, a duty which the more traditional models of professional care overlook or underplay. Not only are professional carers not exempt from the sort of obligations to their clients that you or I have, to treat other people with proper respect; but inasmuch as they are especially concerned with the whole person, and not an arm, a case, a disease and so on, it is the nature and form of their obligations which exemplify moral relationships. Thus professional carers have come to be regarded as having duties to the individual with whom they deal in terms of 'respect for the individual' or 'respect for the individual's autonomy'. They must not simply assume that they, the experts, know best: and even if they do happen to know best they must act as though they did not, because they are not dealing with car engines or the like but with an individual human being, than which nothing more important can be conceived. For if one fails to care about the individual, then that way lies paternalism, alienation and an anti-democratic subordination of the citizen to the bureaucratic machine. On this there appears to be agreement across the political spectrum, from socialist critics of the National Health Service to enthusiastic advocates of privatisation. Not unreasonably, I trust, I characterise this very familiar position as liberal, and the more traditional attitude to which it is opposed as authoritarian. More controversially perhaps, I shall attempt to argue against the liberal model and to suggest that reflection on this aspect of the ethics of caring leads to dissatisfaction with a central element of liberal ethical theory, namely its positing of individuals' wants as an ethical 'given'.

Let us take as an example what might appear to be an entirely unexceptionable statement of the liberal attitude applied to the giving of information, a topic currently central in discussions not only of medical and social work practice but also of schoolteachers' reports, credit assessment companies, the Special Branch, and so on. We all have a right to know, and the relevant experts a duty to tell us, whatever we want to know about our own case, files or records (subject only to certain specified exceptions):

> We have 'a right to know'. There is a duty on the expert to inform his patient as far as he can why the course of action he is recommending to the patient, or is himself carrying out on behalf of the patient, is necessary or desirable. But suppose the patient is not interested, simply does not want to know; or apprehensive, does not want to be made to face up to possibly unwelcome facts? In such cases the expert might not be failing to respect the patient if he withheld information of a kind that we should hold he had in general a duty to give to a patient who demanded it.[1]

There are of course many problems lurking beneath the surface of such an apparently agreeable position. Just how, for example, does the notion of 'rights' work and how useful is it? Or one might well question the viability of the sort of autonomy which serves as the basis of the 'respect' the expert is supposed to have for the patient, as Keith Graham has recently done.[2] But it seems to me that there is something more basic here which underlies and/or informs attitudes such as this, attitudes which rest on the apparently eminently reasonable view that the patient comes first – namely a liberal understanding of 'the individual', an understanding informed primarily by the assumed givenness of wants. I shall start by making some comments about the passage quoted in order to show how 'the individual' informs the analysis offered and how such a notion of the individual is, and must be, closely tied to individuals' wants; and then go on to suggest why individuals' wants are not a proper basis for the doctor-patient, social worker-client, or similar relations.

Setting aside general problems about the idea of rights, why is it thought that one of the rights we have is the 'right to know'? If we do indeed have such a right, then *either* this is the case because knowing is, or is thought to be, a good thing; *or* our having such a right implies that knowing is, or is thought to be, a good thing. But why? Broadly there are two sorts of answer. One is based on ideas of the inviolability of the individual or personal integrity: individuals have a right to know because if the truth is withheld they are not being respected as and in themselves. The other seeks a basis in ideas of social value or some idea of the social good: individuals have a right to know because it is in the interests of society that its members have such a right. A society in which individuals are told the truth is a better society than one where the truth is concealed. Now to return to the example quoted: 'But suppose the patient is not interested, simply does not want to know' and so on. If a particular individual, here a patient, 'does not want to know', then that, apparently, changes the expert's duty: for that duty is directly to the patient. The expert does *not*, after all, have any duty 'to inform his patient'. Rather the expert's duty is to act in accordance with the patient's wishes – with the patient's articulated wishes in fact, 'a duty ... to a patient *who demanded*' information. The view that the expert should act in accordance with what the patient or client wants is of course hardly idiosyncratic – indeed it is the bedrock of the liberal position on the matter. Take this, for instance, from a recent discussion of the role of informed consent in clinical trials: 'But who has the right to deprive another individual of this right [the right to autonomy]? It is the patient's right to choose whether or not s/he wishes to be involved in the decision-making process.'[3] The individual's right to autonomy or, if 'right' is eschewed, the individual's autonomy *tout court*, is sacrosanct. The traditional authoritarian attitude to medical and related practice, that 'the expert knows best' and should therefore take decisions on behalf of the patient or client, overrides the individual's autonomy in a welter of paternalism: liberalism puts this right by reinstating the individual over against the expert. Since it is respecting the patient that counts above all else, the doctor's, nurse's, teacher's or social worker's responsibility to do what they think best – for surely they have such a responsibility, if anyone has – is subject to curtailment by the individual with whom they are dealing. The carer's duty is predicated upon the client's wishes, so that it is what a particular individual wants which creates the duty that others have towards that individual. That, for instance, is why no one should be treated against their wishes, for our bodies are our own for us to do with as we please. Of course there are going to be marginal problems about what to do where there is a difference of opinion between the individual being helped and the helper about what course of action is best. But even if people's wishes might occasionally militate against their best interests, to go against those interests is far preferable to acting God, for that way lies tyranny. Respect for the individual, on the basis of the individual's autonomy, is the only safeguard.

Well, what is it for me to respect Sue Smith? Either what I respect in or about Sue Smith is unique to her or it is not. If it is not, if the object of my respect for her lies in something she shares with others, then that object cannot serve to distinguish her from those others in terms of the respect I have for her. The respect I owe Sue Smith, therefore, is due also to all those others who share the qualities in question with her. If, on the other hand, the qualities in question are unique to Sue Smith, then I cannot see how I can have a duty to respect her because of them: the whole notion of having a *duty* rests on its being universalisable. Otherwise the distinctions between friendship and moral obligation would collapse, and either our obligations would become as arbitrary as our likes and preferences or we would find ourselves with obligations to like certain things about people, rather than respecting those things (whether we like them or not). The qualities on the basis of which I owe Sue Smith respect then, are ones she shares with others. This is of course to state the obvious: it is after all as a human being that I must respect her, and her being human is something she shares with others. What then makes Sue Smith different from all those others to whom I owe respect? For the doctor's or social worker's respect for their client is not just that respect which one human being owes another – otherwise there would be no difference between the carer's particular obligation to the patient or client and general moral obligation. The answer appears to be quite simple, namely that it is in so far as she is a patient or client that the carer has particular obligations to Sue Smith. And it is the liberal model of the carer-client relation that informs the professional ethic governing such relations: the client and the carer (and this is why 'client' is the increasingly preferred word) freely undertake to enter into their relationship; freely undertake to adopt their respective responsibilities to each other; and of course do so only in so far as they want to – compulsory treatment, except for just those cases which cause great problems for the liberal model, such as sections under the Mental Health Act or whooping cough vaccination, is not countenanced, and the British Medical Association has succeeded in maintaining the pre-National Health Service mode of contract whereby doctors, unlike civil servants, cannot be directed to exercise their skills. To some extent of course this liberal ideal of freely undertaken obligation tends to fray at the edges, especially the further down the ladder of social and 'professional' hierarchy one looks: imagine trying to convince most consultants that just the same sort of contract is appropriate for individual hospital cleaners or cooks as for them, or the patient in an expensive private hospital that the porter should be as free to choose whom to transport as the specialist is free to choose whom to treat. Nevertheless it is this model which determines the structure of medical practice, and which many seek to extend into areas such as social and community work.

Since the respective obligations of carer and client are freely undertaken they are undertaken only inasmuch as both parties want to do so. What distinguishes Sue Smith as Dr Jones's patient from Sue Smith as the woman I can see out of the window is what she wants – namely to be treated by Dr Jones. The respect the doctor is supposed to have for her thus amounts to respect for what she wants, since it is what she wants that distinguishes her from others. That of course is why *wants* have come to play such an important part in liberal ethical theory. It is *wants* which constitute the irreducible core of the individual, and so it is *wants* which must lie at the basis of morality. Hence the long-running attempt to show how and why certain moral principles cannot fail to be in accord with what anyone must want; and hence it is that 'the expert might not be failing to respect the patient if he withheld information of a kind that we should hold he had in general a duty to give to a patient who demanded it'. Putting the individual at the centre of one's moral concern is to make what individuals want the central object of that concern: there is nothing else that 'respect for the individual' can consist in, since it is the differences in what you and I want that constitute the differences between you and me as individual objects of moral concern.

What the individual wants however is in itself irrelevant to questions about what ought to be done except in so far as taking such wants into account is conducive to the social good, whether because of the nature of what is wanted in a particular case or because – on broadly rule-utilitarian sorts of grounds – taking even grubby desires into account outweighs in general terms the grubbiness of what is wanted. That is to say that, rather than trying to determine what any rational person must want in an attempt to avoid the sorts of absurdities which arise if one argues that just anything that any individual happens to want is a proper moral consideration, I think that wants – again *per se* – have no moral role. It is not just that what an individual happens to want might not be an overriding consideration (as when, for example, someone might want a doctor to provide them with the means of committing suicide), but that it is no moral consideration at all (aside from the indirect qualification entered above regarding the social good), since morality is a means of ranking wants. My wanting something may constitute a reason for my attempting to obtain it; but where such an attempt gives rise to conflict a moral resolution will consist in subjecting that want to moral assessment and comparison. What people want is certainly part of the data for moral debate, but this is crucially different from its being taken to be (part of) the *moral content* of such debate. It is one thing for what I want to be a reason for my getting it: but quite another for it to be a moral reason for my getting it. The attempt to show that there are things which any rational person must want has, I suggest, failed – and with it the attempt to draw rational limits around the liberal's acceptance of just any wants as allowably constitutive of moral judgment. Liberalism, that is, cannot rationally deal with the moral fanatic's desires.

In the present example then, it may be that there are good reasons why an individual should be told something they do not want to discover, and their not wanting it is relevant only inasmuch as a society in which information is forced on people by doctors and/or others might be a worse society than one where individuals' wants in such matters are taken into account (but nevertheless possibly overriden –

where, for example, the patient's family might have to know the prognosis and be put under intolerable strain by having to conceal it from the patient). Whether or not this is actually the case I do not know: and indeed I have nothing at all to say about the connections between individuals' wants and the interests of society, since I am not attempting to suggest a substantive moral theory but rather only something about what should govern the form of such a theory, namely that one cannot avoid the difficult issue of what sort of society there should be by resorting to the liberal escapism of attending to people's wants.

Either a society in which everyone is compelled 'to be involved in the decision-making process' would be better than one in which it is left to the desires, wishes, preferences or demands of individuals whether they are thus involved; or it would be worse. That is the question which requires resolution. Or consider such related examples as slavery, private education, or prostitution: what those individuals wanted in the 1830s who happened to want to own slaves, or those today who want to send their children to a public school, or those who want to use a prostitute, is morally relevant only in so far as their getting what they want is conducive to the social good: and it is that which, if anything, constitutes the moral grounds on which their wants should or, as in these three cases, should not be satisfied. It is not something's being wanted which is the point, but its character. It might be that a society where the established medical and related practice was to tell the truth, despite the various harms thereby done to certain individuals, would be a better society than one where that was not the practice: just as a society where men were not permitted to have access to prostitutes (because there were not any) or where there was no access to public schools (again because there were not any) would be better than ours – some, but not all, other things being equal.

It is likely to be objected that all I am doing is to insist that it must be people's 'true wants', in some Platonic sense, as opposed to their whims, unreflective wants, passing desires and so on, which must be the basis of moral action.[4] Even if a man does want to use a prostitute, this is not what he 'really' wants or, in a more Aristotelian mode, it is not something which he can rationally want. The point of morality is to uncover what people's true, or rational, wants really are. Are the patient's true wants being met by hiding the truth? Or can the patient rationally or consistently, or without ultimate self-contradiction, want not to be told the truth? The objection is an important one because it helps expose what is at the basis of what is wrong with the liberal position. Who decides what an individual's true wants are? Either true wants or, for that matter, rational wants, are in the end whatever an individual finally decides they are, after suitable reflection, consideration, consultation and so on (the whim, thought through, becomes a real want); or they are not. In the former case, where the individual is left as final arbiter, the situation is the same as with an individual's 'ordinary' wants – they are in the end what the individual says they are, either directly or more circuitously (where the meaning of 'true' or 'rational' rather than what is wanted is ultimately an individual decision). If not, then the individual does not know best and is not the final arbiter of the matter, whether in respect of what is wanted or what is true or rational. In practice of course it tends to be other individuals who make the decisions, which is why liberal respect for the individual comes down to respect for some individuals rather than others, so what is true or what is rational is in the end decided by those individuals who command power. The point is that by hiding behind the rhetoric of the question who knows best if not the individual, the question what *is* best fails to be addressed; and instead of attempting to answer it, however provisionally, inadequately and guardedly, the liberal abandons the responsibility to make the attempt for the safety, intellectual if not political, of the status quo.

Perhaps though, it is people's true *needs* rather than their true wants which is what the issue is really about. After all it is because a patient's true needs are best served by their being kept in a mental hospital that some liberals are prepared to sanction this compulsion, even at the risk of an element of paternalism. But this takes us very close to the authoritarianism of more traditional views of, for instance, the doctor's responsibilities; for adverting to people's needs is precisely to avoid the difficulty of attending to their wants, whereby each individual is the final arbiter of what is right, by allowing the expert the final say. Needs are not private in the way that wants are. This position, the authoritarian as opposed to the liberal, at least has the merit of honesty. In the end the expert knows best. Rather than cut off discussion at that point however, might it not be worth exploring the possibility of more democratic ways of answering the question who knows best, rather than simply responding with the liberal knee-jerk which insists that if it is not the doctor (and it is not) then it must be the client?

Suppose a patient wants to receive a new and extremely expensive form of treatment, wants it very much indeed, since without it they will soon die: a heart transplant, for instance. The question is whether or not they should have what they want, since, for example, the money spent on it would mean not spending a similar sum on fifty other people, ten of whom would die as a consequence. The example is doubtless familiar. But if in this case what a particular individual wants *constitutes* the moral problem, then what are the relevant differences between this case and the earlier example of the truth not being told a patient who does not want to hear it, such that in the latter case what the patient wants does determine what should be done? It cannot be the wanting itself which constitutes such a difference, unless one supposes an extra-ordinarily crude measure of intensity of wanting, a proposal easily disposed of – someone might happen to want some minor cosmetic surgery ever so much but that does not mean that resources should be spent on them rather than on the poor and elderly woman who would very much like a replacement hip, even though the intensity of her wanting might, for all sorts of entirely obvious reasons to do with her poverty, class, gender and age, be less than that of the person who wants a straighter nose. If it is not simply the wanting which makes the difference, then it must be something about what is wanted, that is, something about the sort of thing it is rather than the fact that it is the object of someone's desire.

Consider the example of home as opposed to hospital births. It is often asserted that if a woman wants to have her baby at home, then she ought not to have to go into hospital instead, even if the risks to herself and/or the baby are marginally greater in the case of home births (and I have no view as to whether or not they are, except in so far as much of the evidence usually cited seems, as so often in these debates, either irrelevant or evidence of something quite different). Anyway the view that women should be allowed to have their babies at home if they want to appears quite unexceptionable. But is it? If based on an explicit social policy in the formulation of which due weight is given to mothers, intending mothers, midwives, nurses, doctors, fathers, intending fathers, staff of institutions for handicapped children, all voters and so on, then it may or may not be unexceptionable. But if based on what individual women want (which women?) then it is not: for under what obligations are midwives (and others, such as doctors and ambulance drivers, who might have a role in unfortunate circumstances) who, as individuals, want *not* to help with and/or encourage home births, to go along with those mothers-to-be who want a home birth? If the answer given is that that is part of the job – and there is no other answer if the matter is not one of social policy but of individuals' wants – then what does the liberal propose saying in reply to the midwife whose response is, 'Very well, if that's part of the job I'm giving it up'? The point is of course that the form that duties take within social roles is not, and cannot be, a matter for personal decision in accordance with personal wants. Being a midwife, doctor, teacher, social worker, nurse, lawyer, bricklayer, train driver or shop assistant is possible only within a social context and – hopefully and properly – as a result of social negotiation: but then just the same is true of being a patient, client, student, passenger or shopper. The woman about to give birth is not just, or simply, Sue Smith, the unique individual who is Sue Smith. She is also

Sue Smith who has sought medical advice, who is in a position to have sought it, who has in short adopted a particular role. Now that role might well not be entirely satisfactory (and in this example is indeed often profoundly and importantly unsatisfactory) – but taking political action to bring about changes in and redefinitions of social roles, and to create new ones and abolish current ones, is not to be confused with the demand that one person involved should do as another wants. For if it is *wants* which matter, then one person's are as good as another's.

Another example which comes to mind is the demand for abortion on request: if such a demand fails to take account of those who perform or might perform abortions, then it amounts to no more than an insistence on the primacy of some people's wants as opposed to others', and, crucially, lays itself open to defeat on precisely that score. If it is only because some – however many – women want abortion on demand to be freely available, then there is no good reason why anyone should conform to that desire. The practical outcome is that of a varied and complex power struggle, the 'success' of which might perhaps be the blackmailer blackmailed. If abortion on demand is a good thing, then it is a good thing even if many, even the majority, of women do not wish to avail themselves of the facility or even if they want other women not to do so.

Even if some more Kantian notion of the individual was posited as the basis of individual-centred medical ethics however – a notion much less, if at all, tied to wants – there remain large objections. Consider the following, taken from an unusually well-argued defence of a broadly liberal medical ethics:

> If the physician is morally bound to serve the individual isolated patient, then it is unacceptable for a physician to take actions designed to protect the health of the community as a whole, especially if those actions are not for the benefit of some specific individuals. Yet many public health decisions require certain compromises with the liberty and even the welfare of individuals in order to serve the common welfare of the public.[5]

This hopefully uncontroversial view, intended to save a liberal ethic from the extremes of *laissez-faire* individualism, may appear to be stating what is simply obvious: nevertheless the point is worth making, as it brings out some of the contradiction of liberalism. Nobody becomes a patient, nobody can become a patient, as an individual entity but only as a member of a specific society. 'Patient', 'client' and 'pupil' are social concepts, just like 'thief', 'parent', 'doctor' or 'taxpayer'. To focus on a specific individual as the proper recipient of care is to accept whatever definition happens to hold sway, whatever politics have resulted in this particular individual's having come to be a patient. Equally it is to accept the status quo whereby some people never get to be patients at all but die while waiting; and also to accept that some people get to be patients who ought not to be – the subjects, or rather the objects, of medical experiments in concentration camps or conscripts detailed to act as guinea-pigs during atmospheric nuclear tests.

This is not to suggest that everyone is responsible for everything, *mea culpa* on a grand scale; but to argue that doctors', nurses', social workers', teachers', bank managers' and train drivers' responsibilities extend only to those people who happen to be their patients, clients, pupils, customers and passengers is to advocate that people abrogate the responsibility they have in respect of the practice in which they are engaged. Part of what it is to be, for example, a doctor is to be concerned about medical practice, that is, the context which enables one, materially and logically, to be a doctor: 'patients before politics' not only obscures this but is a piece of nonsense, for politics make 'patients' possible. Attempted collective action to ensure that 'patients' continues to have the sense built up over the last thirty-five years – picketing against private cleaning contractors, for example – harmful as it inevitably is to certain individuals, is met by the sometimes naive, sometimes only too shrewd cry of 'patients before politics';[6] naive objection to political action unites with the *laissez-faire* advocacy of private medicine (or education or welfare service or transport) by means of a common assumption that it is the individual – some a-historical, entirely abstract and deliberately unnamed individual – who matters; and the only difference is that liberals tend to think that all, or at any rate most, individuals matter whereas their conservative opponents are quite clear that some individuals matter more than others (hence the latter's disdain for theorising, a practice which they at least know to be a sham).

Furthermore caring about individuals opens up the possibility, or indeed the necessity, of *not* caring about other individuals – a paradox which helps to establish practices which have just those results with which we are familiar from the concentration camps: some individuals may be thought not to be worth caring about because they are thought not 'really' to be individual examples of the species at all (just as, in the case of attending to individuals' wants, some people's wants are regarded as less important than others). Not caring *about* any particular individuals however is not open to this abuse, because people may then be cared *for* regardless of the individual they happen to be, as it is in the community's best interest that this be done. The objection will of course be made that this emphasis on the community's interest produces just that state of affairs to which I myself have just objected, namely the sort of things which went on in concentration camps. As a matter of fact, this happens: but this, the community's interest, is just what needs to be explicitly addressed. Attention to individuals deflects from this, and permits situations to arise by default which some ideologies advocate explicitly. To hide behind 'the individual' is to evade political responsibility in favour of maintaining the present configuration of the community's interest, of maintaining the power of those who presently determine what the community's interest consists in.[7]

What is more, the liberal insistence on the individual's coming before all other considerations without seeking to justify such a practice in terms of the community's best interests (though of course some liberals are hard-line rule-utilitarians) renders the expert's role impossible. Either a person has a particular expertise or not; and either society has agreed with such a person on the specific role of that expertise or not. But the only conceivable point of an expert role – and I am not here arguing whether or not there should be such roles, for that Illichian issue is a separate one – is that the exercise of such a role tends to the overall good of society. But if that is so, if experts have a proper role to play, then to ask them to abrogate the responsibility to take decisions, itself after all an integral part of that expertise, is absurd. Imagine demanding that a skilled bricklayer exercise that skill in building a wall on foundations he knows to be inadequate. Part of the role of 'doctor', 'social worker' or 'teacher' is precisely to take on a degree of responsibility on behalf of people who either do not have the requisite knowledge or are not in a condition to exercise their judgment as well as otherwise they might. Just what that degree is, and how much, if at all, this consideration applies to which experts, are just the sort of political decisions that need to be made.

To go back to the earlier example of truth-telling: either the doctor or someone else (who, I wonder?) has to find out whether the person in front of them does or does not want to know; is or is not interested; is experiencing this or that degree of apprehension. But that process of finding out will itself contribute to the patient's wishes, feelings and so on, in the matter: merely being asked if I want to know about my condition might well make me more apprehensive about it. Now either the doctor works on a minimalist model, saying nothing unless explicitly asked ('a patient who demanded [the truth]') – which puts an enormous, and I would have thought entirely insupportable, degree of responsibility on the patient as well as providing a hopelessly wide get-out clause for the doctor; or the doctor asks the patient what they want to know – eliciting either the response, 'everything', or giving rise to the earlier situation; or the doctor asks the patient whether or not they want to know something specific – a procedure either again creating massive pressure for the patient or one which is obviously self-defeating, if the intention is to ask a straight question.

What all this amounts to is this: either doctors act authoritarianly in insisting on their patients' complete responsibility; or covertly paternalistically by fixing the question so that the patient has the impression of acting freely or autonomously when clearly they are not. That this should be so is of course not surprising: liberalism tends generally to collapse into covert paternalism. The liberal antipathy to rules and to defined roles leaves those individuals who are powerful to determine what is possible for the rest.

## Notes

An earlier draft of this paper was read at a conference on Ethical Issues about Caring, Manchester, September 1984, and I should like to thank participants for their helpful discussion from which this paper has, I hope, benefited.

1   Thomas McPherson (1984) 'The moral patient', *Philosophy*, 55, 228 (April), p. 179.
2   'Moral autonomy and political organisation' (1984), read at the Annual Conference of the Society for Applied Philosophy, Isle of Thorns, May.
3   Carolyn Faulder (1983), 'Can being told the truth seriously damage your health?' read at the Workshop on Philosophical and Ethical Issues in Medicine, Manchester, November. She expands on her position in her interesting and timely *Whose Body Is It: the troubling issue of informed consent* (1985). London, Virago.
4   This was pointed out to me by Chris Cherry, to whom thanks are due for his helpful comments on an earlier draft of this paper.
5   Robert M. Veatch (1981), *A Theory of Medical Ethics* New York, Basic Books, p. 157.
6   See my 'Striking responsibilities' (1985), *Journal of Medical Ethics*, 11, 2, (June), pp. 66–9.
7   The problem is of course a familiar one: the argument parallels, among others, the case for economic sanctions against South Africa.

# 5 Shall we care for you or do you want to work?

*Trevor Owen*

In the context of this volume I find myself the odd man out. An industrialist will inevitably feel somewhat overawed in the company of professors, philosophers, social scientists, medical people and counsellors, particularly when they are people of such distinction. And an industrialist is what I am. I worked for ICI for twenty-three years and have now (1982) completed four years as Managing Director of Remploy; and I ought perhaps to start by explaining what sort of an organisation Remploy is.

Remploy, like ICI, is an industrial concern. We employ eleven thousand people in ninety-four factories from Aberdeen to Penzance. We have a turnover close on £50 million and provide a wide range of goods and services. We assemble music centres and bind books; we make jerseys for Marks and Spencer and wheelchairs for the DHSS; we make beds, shelving systems for libraries and warehouses, cartons and boxes; we assemble the steering columns for the Mini and the Metro; and we made the protective clothing which shielded our soldiers and sailors from flash and burn in the Falklands. This year we started producing lettuces and in 1983 we hope to start making ice cream – at the rate of 150 choc bars a minute.

Except for its diversity, Remploy is very little different from any other industrial enterprise of its size and the sort of things which I worry about as chief executive – sales, productivity, industrial relations, cash flow – are no different from the sort of things any other chief executive worries about in these difficult times.

The same thing can be said about the people I employ. Their concerns are about having the right sort of job and getting paid fairly for it. They want to have congenial people to work with and in particular reasonable managers and supervisors. They get fed up from time to time and when they do they call upon their trade unions to help them do something about it. They are in fact no different from the rest of the country's workforce. Except, perhaps, in one minor respect. Nearly nine thousand of the people employed in Remploy are severely disabled; indeed it was with the specific purpose of employing severely disabled people that Remploy was established immediately after the last war.

The disabilities themselves vary enormously. Only about 15 per cent come into the category which people nowadays most easily recognise as disabled – amputees, paraplegics, arthritics and spinal injury cases; 10 per cent are blind or deaf; 10 per cent have got severe heart or related conditions; 35 per cent have got mental disabilities in the very broadest sense ranging from mental subnormality to epilepsy, schizophrenia, neurosis and other psychological disorders.

Any disability which makes it virtually impossible in these unenlightened days for someone to get a job in open industry, even under the terms of the 3 per cent quota, makes an individual eligible to work for Remploy. And that is where the link to the caring professions comes in. The condition of people who work for Remploy does of course vary tremendously but some have little personal mobility; some find difficulty in looking after themselves and live in hostels; many are in pain twenty-four hours a day; one of them is not only deaf but blind as well.

Many people therefore assume, not unreasonably, that Remploy is itself a 'caring organisation'. We are not. Visiting American professors assume that our factory managers will be equipped at least with a higher degree in counselling or with some equivalent qualification – but they are not. If they have a recognised educational qualification at all it will most probably be an ACMA or an HND in business studies, but they are just as likely to be time-served fitters who have come up through the ranks of supervision to management. Their experience and training is not as carers but as managers. And that is how it should be. The essence of Remploy is normality. We make perfectly normal products in perfectly normal factory conditions and to do so we employ perfectly normal people. The abnormality of the people who work for Remploy is in the minds of a cruel and unthinking society, not in them.

They do of course happen to be disabled but so are most of us. There is a colossal range of activities which I, for instance, am either physically or mentally not equipped to perform. Nuclear physics is quite beyond me unfortunately and, even more sadly, my fantasy of playing stand-off half for Wales is unlikely ever to be fulfilled – but that does not prevent me from living a full and normal life. What I *cannot* do does not really matter. It is what I *can* do that counts.

That is the framework within which Remploy operates. In a sense we are not interested in disability. If you are a paraplegic we shall put you at a bench and teach you to operate an industrial sewing machine, and your disability becomes irrelevant. If you are educationally sub-normal we shall teach you a repetitive task at a machine. It will take time for you to learn it but, when you have done so, no one can do that task better than you. Where then is the disability?

This seems to me to be a very straightforward and practical way of dealing with what can be, if you choose to make it, a most intractable and distressing problem.

It can, of course, shock people.

> One candidate for employment in a Remploy factory was a seventeen-year-old boy who had had a hole in his chest from birth. He was accepted after an interview and told to report for work the following Monday. When he did so the factory manager called him in to decide where to place him in the factory. 'Let's see,' said the factory manager, 'what problems do you have that I need to take account of in finding a job for you here?' Slightly shaken, the young man started to unbutton his shirt. 'Yes, yes,' said the factory manager, 'I know all about that. But do you have any *problems*? Is there anything that you're not going to be able to do?' When I visited the factory some three weeks later, the factory manager introduced us with the comment, 'This is Mike. He's new. We've been trying him out on various jobs in the factory' (it was a furniture factory) 'and he seems to be able to do just about everything. He'll be pretty good.'

That young man had never been treated in that way in all his life. He had spent seventeen years being cared for. It had diminished him. He was fortunately still young enough to be rescued from the grips of his carers and restored to normality.

Let me give you a second example, at the other end of the age scale.

> Cora had been, as a young woman, already totally crippled with arthritis. She was put to be cared for in a Cheshire Home. She was both happy and extremely well looked after there but had in reality little to look forward to. When a Remploy factory started up in her area she was persuaded to see if she could manage the physical problems involved in holding down a factory job. It was a sewing factory and she started in a corner of the factory tackling jobs that were physically very simple. She was extremely slow at first but gradually improved, went on to the sewing machines and eventually became a highly skilled operator.
>
> Cora was very bright and in due course it was decided to promote her to chargehand. She refused the promotion on the grounds that she did not think that a chargehand should be dependent on being pushed around the factory in a wheelchair.
>
> Personally I think she was mistaken in that but I respect the decision she made and I respect even more the consequences of her decision.
>
> She decided that, if she was thought capable of being a chargehand, then that is what she would like to do; but first she would have to be able to walk. So slowly, and with infinite pain, she taught herself to walk.
>
> I met her at the end of her career, to present her with her farewell gifts on her retirement. She was then a chargehand. She was walking – with two sticks and with some difficulty, but she walked. She had a BEM from the Queen. She was married and was retiring to her own house nearby to look after the house and her husband and, of course, to care for herself.

Remploy's great contribution to this remarkable story was to do nothing. Nothing at all. She did it all for herself. All we did was to refuse point blank to care for her – and so provide the opportunity through which she rehabilitated herself into normal society.

My experience at Remploy leads me to suspect that our society has a tendency to indulge itself in caring too much, to the detriment both of the carers and of those who are the object of care. Caring is an activity bestowed by an active human being on a passive object. You care for your garden, your clothes and your car – and the results make you feel good. Or, if it is another human being that is the object of care, then he or she is neither required nor expected to contribute any active response.

There is absolutely nothing you can do in the process of being cared for other than feel grateful. That gives a nice warm feeling to the care-giver but it is not generally a socially constructive transaction and it is one which runs the risk of diminishing both parties.

I do not deny, of course, that there are circumstances when human beings need and must have care. The very young, the very old, the very sick, the very disabled – they may not be able to survive without care and the people who provide such care are essential to the maintenance of a civilised society. But I do plead for a greater degree of discrimination in the use of caring than we have at present. Care is essential for the helpless, but one of the things that Remploy's experience shows is that not all those who are in receipt of care flourish on it.

We in Remploy offer an alternative to care. We offer work, and in doing that we offer respect. We respect the individual, however disabled he or she may be, for the ordinary fulfilled human being that he or she is or can be; and we present him or her with the challenge to continue to merit that respect by the sort of contribution which he or she can make, on their own terms as much as on ours.

I accept of course that in writing of Remploy I am dealing with an extremely narrow and specialised segment of that population which might be thought to be in need of care.

It may be nevertheless that the lessons have wider application. One of my most interesting and rewarding experiences over the last couple of years has been to serve as a member of Peter Barclay's working party enquiring into the role and tasks of social workers on behalf of the National Institute for Social Work.[1] In the course of this project I had the opportunity of going round with a number of social workers as they went about their daily work. It was a most valuable part of my education and left me, incidentally, with an immense admiration for social workers and what they do. Some of them get things wrong from time to time, of course (the same can be said of managing directors), but in general I found myself observing highly professional and dedicated people who knew very well what they were doing and how to do it. My best hope for social workers is that they can now stop being investigated and be allowed to get on with the job.

But that is by the way. What may be relevant to my present theme are a pair of contrasting illustrations of problem families:

> Mr and Mrs T. were clearly unable to cope. Their house was a shambles, the television and much of the household furniture had been repossessed because of non-payment of the HP, they were in debt and their son was in trouble with the police. After considerable heart-searching the son was put into care and the parents were taken, with a number of other couples who were having difficulty in coping, into a residential home where they were set to cope under supervision.
>
> Each couple was obliged in turn to do the housework and the catering for the whole household. They had to get it right, they had to provide and the money had to last. There was some simple input from the staff and there were group discussions between all the participants on the events of each day so that those whose turn it was to cope could get feed-back and help.
>
> When I visited Mrs T. with the social worker, she and her husband had come to the end of their residential course. I met her in her new home standing in front of a large television set beaming happily. They now knew how to manage, she said, they were never going to be in debt again – and their son was coming home that very day.

Contrast that with a different visit:

> Miss B. was a former nurse who lived with her two daughters aged eleven and thirteen on the third floor of a Victorian house converted into flats. She was an unkempt woman of fiftyish, still in her night clothes in the middle of the afternoon. She suffered from agoraphobia and never left the flat. She kept the children off school on Mondays so that they could do the shopping for her. 'After all,' she said, 'I can't be expected to do it myself.' She appeared to spend most of the time on the phone to various council officials and was full of complaints about how little they would do for her.
>
> The social worker had battled hard and long, and ultimately successfully, to get her this flat instead of the damp and unsavoury place which she and her children had lived in before, but felt a sense of failure because it was up three flights of stairs. She felt Miss B. would have more contact with the world if she could manage to get her shifted to a ground floor flat instead and she was now working hard on this project.

I do not want to criticise the social worker in either of these cases. How can I tell what is right or wrong from half an hour's discussion? Nevertheless I have to confess that I was left with some feeling of unease about the social worker's approach in the second case, even though I could have nothing but admiration for her devotion and dedication.

It seemed to me that Miss B. had been cared for to the point where her only interest in life was just that – being cared for. Mrs T. on the other hand had learnt that she could make a good world for herself or a bad one – and that the choice was hers. The process of learning that particular lesson had not been easy for her, but it had been worth it.

I have therefore some suspicion of one-sided caring as forming the basis of any relationship between two individuals. Like any other drug it may sometimes be necessary but, like any other drug, it should be used sparingly.

I also note in passing (although I am by now some way outside my area of competence) that unalloyed caring can be destructive of the carer too. It does not seem to be a natural condition for a human being to find himself in. I have a lot of respect for a friend of mine who is employed to deal with emotionally-deprived children, who commented to me recently: 'If one of them says, "Why are you always picking on me?" I say, "I'm not. You just piss me off!" *I do allow myself,*' she said, *the luxury of real feelings from time to time.*'

And reality is what in the end it is all about. Caring, when it is a protection of the helpless from harm, must be something which is to be valued and which we would all like to see developed and enhanced to the benefit of our society. Caring though can sometimes be no more than sheltering people from reality, and then it seems to me to be a much more dubious activity.

We in Remploy believe the greatest service we can provide to the disabled people we employ is to present them with reality and not to shelter them from it.

Earlier I wrote that Remploy was not a caring organisation. Perhaps that is to put it too starkly. Epileptic fits are an everyday occurrence in our factories. Our managers deal with that as a matter of course and must equally be able to take in their stride the days when someone tries to commit suicide in the toilets, or any of a multitude of emergencies which would make the hair of most other factory managers stand on end. Certainly they know the telephone numbers of the local doctor and the social services department better than that of Remploy's head office.

So yes, we have to care and we do care; but we do not let it show too much and care is not primarily what we offer to the people who come to us.

Severely disabled people are of course entitled to be cared for if they want to. The lesson to be learnt from Remploy is that most of them prefer to work.

## Note

1   The report was published as *Social Workers, their role and tasks* (1982). London, Bedford Square Press for NISW.

# 6  Paternalism and caring

*Richard Lindley*

I suppose the traditional image of a doctor or other caring professional is as a benevolent paternalist – someone who knows best how to look after his (for traditionally professionals were male) patients or clients. It was not thought that there was anything wrong with paternalism as such indeed it was welcomed and admired. Nowadays there has been a significant shift in the climate of opinion, so that in liberal circles 'paternalism' is almost a dirty word. Doctors, nurses and social workers may be *accused* of being paternalistic, and they are likely to try to defend themselves by rejecting the allegation. But what is wrong with paternalistic intervention among carers? I am sure that on reflection few people would think it is unacceptable in all circumstances. Let us begin with a story from ancient Greek mythology.

The story of Theseus and the Minotaur of Knossos ends in tragedy – the death of the hero's father, Aegeus. Theseus had agreed at the start of his voyage that, if he succeeded, he would hoist a white sail on his homecoming ship. Otherwise the ship would return home powered by its original black sail. Theseus slew the Minotaur, and after various other distractions and adventures, set sail for home. Sadly he forgot to swap the sails, and Aegeus, who spied the ship in the distance, naturally assumed that Theseus had been lost in a failed mission. According to one version of the myth, despondent, he committed suicide by leaping off the Acropolis.

Let us suppose you knew (it does not matter how) the truth about Theseus's success. Benevolent concern for Aegeus at least gives you a good reason to try to tell him Theseus is safe and triumphant, before it is too late. But suppose you cannot persuade him in time (either because of a language problem or because he just cannot believe you, a stranger). For Aegeus to delay would, in ancient Athens, be shameful.

I think that in these circumstances respect for Aegeus would justify using physical restraint on him, even the administration of a narcotic which would prevent him from harming himself until he could see Theseus with his own eyes. In so far as such restraint is motivated by concern for Aegeus it is paternalistic. If it would be right to stop Aegeus, by force if necessary, then not all paternalistic intervention is unjustified. Indeed it may sometimes be *required* by benevolent concern.

In this chapter I am searching for principles which may be helpful for sorting out justified from unjustified paternalism in personal relations, public policy and legal statute. In order to begin this task I need an adequate conception of paternalism. Attempts to define the concept have not been entirely successful in giving an accurate analysis of what people have in mind when they use the word. Consider, for example, Gerald Dworkin's (1972, p. 78) rather too restrictive definition of paternalism in his very influential paper: 'the interference with a person's liberty of action justified by reasons referring exclusively to the welfare, good, happiness, needs, interests or values of the person being coerced'.

Bernard Gert and Charles Culver (1976 and 1982) pointed out that not all cases of (obviously) paternalistic behaviour restrict a person's *liberty of action*. Consider two examples, which I have based on theirs. First, a woman lies on her deathbed and asks you, her doctor, to tell her what has become of her son, whom she will never meet again as he lives on the other side of the world. You know that he has just been declared redundant, his marriage has broken up and in his misery he has become alcoholic. In order to spare her pain you lie to her, saying that he is doing well. In this case there is no interference with her liberty of action, although it appears to be a clear case of paternalism. In the second example a doctor administers a blood transfusion to an unconscious Jehovah's Witness road accident victim, who will die without the transfusion. He knows the Witness would choose death in preference to the transfusion, but because he judges that continued life is more in the patient's interests than an untimely death, he goes ahead with the treatment anyway. The doctor's behaviour appears to be almost a paradigm of paternalistic intervention; yet there is, once again, no restriction on the patient's liberty of action.

These cases share with paternalistic restrictions on people's liberty of action an apparent conflict between what the person who is the object of the paternalistic behaviour wants, and what is best for her. It is sometimes described as a conflict between respect for autonomy and concern to maximise welfare. Paternalistic behaviour typically includes the overriding or disregarding of what its supposed beneficiary wants, in order to promote her or his welfare. Paternalistic behaviour thus has two legs:

1   The agent is motivated by respect for the person who is the intended beneficiary of the act.
2   The will of this person (that is, his or her current overall preference) is either disregarded or overridden by the agent.

Having acknowledged that paternalism extends beyond restrictions of people's liberty of action, I want to point out that my central concern in this chapter is with paternalistic restrictions of this kind.

The concept of 'respect for the person' is elusive but crucial. Respect for someone may give you a reason to override her will in order to protect her interests, as when one stops a young child from playing on a busy road. On the other hand respect may give you a reason *not* to force someone to abandon a self-harming practice, on the grounds that to do so would be an intolerable violation of his autonomy.

This chapter lacks theoretical elegance because I find myself in the no-man's-land between two elegant, extreme but in the end implausible, views about when paternalism might be justified. According to the first, paternalistic behaviour should be absolutely prohibited (with no exceptions). This view is suggested by the following oft-quoted statement by John Stuart Mill (1859, p. 72), although it was by no means unequivocally endorsed by its author:

> the only purpose for which power can be rightfully exercised over any member of a civilised community against his will, is to prevent harm to others. His own good, either physical or moral, is not a sufficient warrant. He cannot rightfully be compelled to do or forbear because it will be better for him to do so, because it will make him happier, because in the opinion of others, to do so would be wise, or even right. These are good reasons for remonstrating with him, or reasoning with him, or persuading him, but not for compelling him, or visiting him with any evil in case he do otherwise . . . Over himself, his own body and mind, the individual is sovereign.

This is about restrictions on people's liberty of action, but the reasons for opposing these restrictions could apply with equal force to paternalistic deceptions and other overriding of people's wills (for example the Jehovah's Witness case).

Perhaps the main reason for opposing paternalism stems from a belief that autonomy (controlling one's own life) is a vital interest of human beings. Although I recognise the importance of autonomy I believe that exceptionless prohibitions are in general suspect, because they may subvert the substantive values which led to the prohibition in the first place. To see the difficulties of an exceptionless prohibition of paternalism, consider the following case.

John is a dramatic person who has just been told by his girl friend that she wants to end their relationship. He is desperately depressed and is about to jump off a bridge. Suppose that if he jumps it is most likely that he will suffer very serious, though not fatal injuries. You realise that if he leaps he will probably have to spend most of his life paralysed in a hospital bed, bitterly regretting his action. His autonomy will be destroyed.

If you were bound by an absolute prohibition on paternalistic action, then if you failed to *persuade* John not to jump you would be unable to prevent him, by force if necessary, from making the disastrous leap. The most likely effect of your non-intervention would be that John's interests in his own autonomy were harmed more than they would have been by a forcible intervention. Your respect for John's autonomy would apparently lead you knowingly to behave in a way which is worse for John's autonomy than a recognised alternative. The exceptionless prohibition leads to conduct which undermines the value which gives it its point.

At the other extreme is mental state act (msa) utilitarianism. According to this view the only things which are intrinsically good or bad are conscious experiences (notably pleasant and painful experiences) or mental states. A right action is simply one which, overall, produces the best net aggregate of pleasant mental states. According to msa utilitarianism autonomy is worth respecting only in so far as it is necessary to maximise pleasure and minimise pain (in what follows, unless I make a specific exception I mean by 'maximise pleasure', 'produce the greatest net amount of pleasure over pain'). If a particular paternalistic act really would maximise pleasure, then it cannot be wrong to perform it, even if to do so is against the wishes of its intended beneficiary, and for the benefit of nobody else.

I believe that msa utilitarianism is wrong in its failure to recognise the intrinsic (non-instrumental) value of autonomy. To see if you believe that autonomy should be respected, apart from its contribution to pleasant states of consciousness, consider the following example, taken from Jonathan Glover (1977), a philosopher by no means unsympathetic to utilitarianism. Suppose there is a man serving a life sentence in gaol with no prospect of parole. He has no family or friends who would be sad if he died sooner rather than later. Given his personality and the conditions in the gaol it is most likely that the rest of his life will contain more misery than pleasure. The sooner he dies the smaller will be the net aggregate of pain in his life. In spite of all this he still wants to go on living. If you were able to kill him painlessly then, according to msa utilitarianism the only reasons not to do so would come from unpleasant side-effects (for example you might be caught, or become corrupted so that you kill people even when it would not maximise pleasure). Those who believe it would certainly be wrong to kill the prisoner, even if there were no harmful side-effects, might well have a different view if the prisoner actually *wanted* you to give him a lethal overdose. Anyone who believes that in this case the wishes of the prisoner are directly (that is, independently of side-effects) relevant to what you should do, accepts that autonomy is of intrinsic value and that respect for a person sometimes requires one to put to one side concern for a person's pleasure in order to respect his autonomy.

The view which I wish to defend rejects the absolutism implicit in Mill's principle, while recognising that autonomy has direct value. The problem is to accord a due weight to respect for autonomy, which does not depend on recourse to obviously *ad hoc* hypotheses. (For a full account of the general difficulty of giving a due weight to autonomy see Lindley, 1986, Pt II.)

I shall now return to Mill, for in spite of the fact that his liberty principle, if taken literally, is too extreme, his work sheds considerable light upon these murky waters. Mill was not in fact an uncompromising absolutist about paternalism. His support for the liberty principle was founded on the belief that the adoption of such a self-denying ordinance by holders of state authority would be the best way of promoting human happiness. Indeed, in *On Liberty* Mill specifically mentions two exceptions to the general prohibition on paternalism. In the paragraph immediately following the statement of the liberty principle quoted above, Mill writes:

> It is, perhaps, hardly necessary to say that this doctrine is meant to apply only to human beings in the maturity of their faculties. We are not speaking of children, or of young persons below the age which the law may fix as that of manhood or womanhood. Those who are still in a state to require being taken care of by others, must be protected against their own actions as well as against external injury. (Mill, 1859, p. 73)

Mill's other specific exception to his principle is stated towards the end of *On Liberty*. He judges that it is morally permissible, for paternalistic reasons, forcibly to prevent someone inadvertently walking on to an unsafe bridge:

> If either a public officer or anyone else saw a person attempting to cross a bridge which had been ascertained to be unsafe, and there was no time to warn him of the danger, they might seize him and turn him back, without any real infringement of his liberty; for liberty consists in doing what one desires, and he does not desire to fall into the river. (ibid. p. 151f)

I shall discuss children later, but first the incautious bridge crosser. If one were unable to convince him in time that the bridge was dangerous (perhaps he speaks no English), the case would, in a crucial respect, be similar to that of Aegeus. We may assume that Mill's person wants to step on to the bridge only on the supposition that it is safe, whereas Aegeus wants to kill himself only on the supposition that Theseus has failed to kill the Minotaur.

I am sure that Mill is right to allow that it would be right to stop the incautious bridge crosser from stepping on to the bridge, by force if necessary, were one unable to convince him of the danger. However it is disingenuous to deny that this would constitute a genuine infringement of liberty. Admittedly he does not want to fall into the river (unless he wants to commit suicide or has some other idiosyncratic project), and falling into the river will be a consequence of stepping on to the bridge. However he most certainly *does* want to step on to the bridge. To seize him and turn him back may well be justifiable in the circumstances, but it is certainly stopping him from doing what he wants – and this is a paradigm case of liberty restriction.

In both the Aegeus and the bridge crosser cases the intervention is justified because without it the object of the intervention would act on the basis of demonstrably false beliefs. I believe that actions premissed on false beliefs are *ipso facto* less than autonomous. If this is so one could argue that, although in the two cases mentioned the interventions do restrict someone's *liberty*, they infringe nobody's *autonomy*, since Aegeus and the bridge crosser would not have been able to act autonomously, even without the interventions.

More difficult issues are raised by the problem of paternalism for children, and it is to this issue that I now turn, before returning to the general problem of why autonomy matters and how it should be treated when it conflicts with other values.

According to Mill the rationale for permitting paternalism towards children is that they 'are still in a state to *require* being taken care of by others'. 'Children' includes not just infants but all those 'below the age which the law may fix as that of manhood or womanhood' (usually somewhere between sixteen and twenty-one). What, in this context, is meant by 'require'? To say that children require to be taken care of by others is to point out that this is a necessary condition for something. But what? One is inclined to say 'for the realisation of their own good'. But children are not the only people who are incapable of realising their own good. Anyway, according to Mill's principle, a person's own good is never a sufficient warrant for overriding her autonomy. If this is true in the case of incompetent adults, then why not in that of children? Or to put it another way, if paternalism is justifiable to promote the good of children why is it in general not so for incompetent adults? Mill is at least aware of a possible difficulty here. He writes:

> If protection against themselves is confessedly due to children and persons under age, is not society equally bound to afford it to persons of mature age who are equally incapable of self-government? If gambling, or drunkenness, or incontinence, or idleness, or uncleanliness, are just as injurious to happiness, and as great a hindrance to improvement, as many or most of the acts prohibited by law, why (it may be asked) should not law, so far as it is consistent with practicability and social convenience, endeavour to repress these also? (ibid. p. 137)

He begins his answer by pointing out that much imprudent behaviour leads people to fail to discharge their obligations to others, causing them harm. It is therefore, despite appearances, not properly included within the liberty principle. He then returns to the main issue: 'the strongest of all the arguments against the interference of the public with purely personal conduct is that, when it does interfere, the odds are that it interferes wrongly, and in the wrong place' (ibid. p. 138). What would it be then, to interfere rightly, and in the right place? One can only surmise that this would be to act genuinely in the best overall interests of the person concerned. The history of adults' treatment of children should not inspire one with confidence that they are more likely to interfere rightly on the right occasions in the lives of (certainly older) children, than they are in those of incompetent adults.

In order to avoid the charge of 'ageism', those who believe that paternalism is justifiable for children but not for incompetent adults must be able to specify the relevant differences between children and adults.

On this score it could be argued that children tend to be especially ignorant about what is in their best interests and about how to pursue successfully already identified interests. Also, children tend to be less prudent than most adults, being influenced to a greater extent by immediate attractions. Being weaker than adults children are prime targets for exploitation by adults, and given their inexperience, stand in special need of protection.

Although these claims are plausible as rough generalisations, it is simply not true that all children under the age of majority are less competent than all adults above it who fall within the scope of Mill's liberty principle. The fact that *all children* are excluded from the liberty principle appears to be unfair either to competent children who do not need 'protection' or to incompetent adults who do. The relevant difference between those who should be subject to state paternalism and those who should not seems to be competence rather than age (which at best is a rough indicator of competence).

There is however something to be said for fixed ages of majority, because the law, of necessity, is not able to make the fine distinctions between individual cases which can be made within private morality. If most children do need paternalistic protection in a way in which most adults do not and the costs of calculating individual exceptions are high, there is a utilitarian reason for accepting Mill's view that children as a whole should be treated separately from adults. Making this distinction between children and adults might be the best way of maximising the successful pursuit of (everyone's) interests.

Nevertheless such an argument carries far less weight in the sphere of personal relationships. For here the costs of considering each case on its individual merits are much lower, and in any case it would be bizarre to try to base one's personal relationships entirely on neutral generalisations about categories of people.

In the personal sphere paternalism may be necessary to protect anyone (adult or child) who really is in a state to require being taken care of by others. Sometimes such an intervention may be a *duty* derived from respect for the person. Thus, if I respected someone (or cared about her at all), I should prevent her, by force if necessary, from leaping off the top of Westminster Cathedral in the belief that she, being Supergirl, could fly over London.

To harm someone is to damage one or more of their interests. Mill was right to point out that people have basic interests not only in having pleasant experiences, but also in autonomy; hence the horror of the society described in Aldous Huxley's *Brave New World*. It is however a mistake to assume that autonomy interests should *always* take precedence over interests in pleasant experiences. There may be occasions where it is better that someone's autonomy be compromised in order to prevent her from suffering pain.

## Autonomy and why it matters

'Autonomy' has its etymological roots in the two Greek words for 'self' and 'rule', and it was in ancient Greece that autonomy was first spoken of as valuable. It was common for Greek cities to seek autonomy – their inhabitants wanted to be free from rule by another power to govern themselves. The autonomy that concerns us here – personal autonomy – is analogous to the autonomy of a city or state, in that personal autonomy requires an individual to be able to choose what to do, and to be free from domination by the will of others. And this requires that the individual at least has the capacity to make choices.

All creatures are either rational or non-rational in the sense of having the capacity for choice. Thus stones, trees and ants are all non-rational since they, we may presume, lack the capacity to base their behaviour on reasons. All human beings except the very young, the severely mentally handicapped and the severely demented, are rational. This should not blind us to the fact that we are all to a greater or lesser extent *irrational*. To be *irrational* requires that one is at least *rational* in the sense just described. Let us call this capacity to exercise choice a 'will'. Thus all human beings, except for those already mentioned, possess a will, whereas most animals and all plants lack a will.

The fact that human beings possess a will means that they are able to form their own conceptions of the sorts of life they would like to lead. When people speak of the need to respect one another's autonomy, they often mean that we should allow people to live their own lives as they choose, even if it does not fit in with our own conception of a good or worthwhile life. The capacity to choose distinguishes us from the brutes, and to deny someone the chance to exercise the capacity (to act autonomously) is to treat her as less than human.

It is something like this reasoning which underlies much opposition to medical paternalism of the sort where a doctor fails to discuss genuine options with a patient and just does what he thinks is best without acting on, or even bothering to discover, the patient's wishes. Most of us would like to be able to make our own personal life-affecting decisions. Even if the decisions I make are not the best decisions, at least they are mine.

Nevertheless the mere fact that human beings, perhaps uniquely, possess a certain capacity, does not *entail* that there is value in the development and exercise of that capacity. Is there anything to be said to someone who is unimpressed by the alleged significance of making one's own decisions? Suppose someone argues that it is irrational to insist that people should make their own decisions, even if someone else is in a position to make better ones on their behalf.

First there is the Millian point that on the whole, despite possible appearances to the contrary, people are likely to make better decisions in regard to their own lives than are other people. On the whole paternalistic intervention is not worth the high risk of failure. This however does not rest on the claim that making one's own decisions is intrinsically desirable, but merely that it is desirable as a means to some other end.

A second strategy is to appeal to people's preferences – not just to their actual preferences, but to the preferences they would have were they perfectly well informed and not irrational. It is plausible to surmise that under these conditions the vast majority of people would value their autonomy. Hence the attractiveness of Mill's remark: 'It is better to be Socrates dissatisfied than a fool satisfied'. However, even if autonomous rational people would prefer to remain autonomous and rational, even if this cost them some satisfaction, it does not follow that autonomy is good for those lacking autonomy who do not particularly care about whether they are autonomous.

I think that probably all attempts to demonstrate that something is intrinsically valuable, where this is meant to be rationally compelling for even the strongest sceptic, are futile. I do hope at least for an agreement among the people who read this chapter that autonomy is something which they value for its own sake.

Yet it certainly does not follow from the proposition that autonomy is intrinsically valuable that people should always be allowed (let alone encouraged) to do just what they want. There are three reasons for this. First the exercise of autonomy is not the only object of intrinsic value in the universe. Secondly a current choice might not be autonomous. Finally a current choice, even if autonomous, might itself be damaging to autonomy (either the agent's or that of someone else). I shall consider each in turn.

## Other values

I have just claimed that it is impossible to *prove* that something valued really has intrinsic worth. The most, perhaps, that can be done, is to point out that some things are (almost) universally desired not as a means to some further end. All I want to do here is to point out that there are things other than autonomy that you, the reader, believe to have intrinsic value. The most important, perhaps, are pleasure and the absence of pain. Although pain may be a good thing as an indicator of organic malfunction or as a character-builder (though its merits in this area are sometimes exaggerated), people do not want pain for its own sake. On the other hand, apart from possibly harmful side-effects, people do want pleasure for its own sake. Mental state utilitarianism is not a completely crazy theory.

If pleasure and the avoidance of pain are intrinsically valuable, then there will be occasions when two intrinsic values – autonomy and pleasure – will conflict. Sometimes it will be right to sacrifice autonomy for pleasure, especially on those occasions when only a little autonomy need be sacrificed for a huge gain in pleasure.

The easiest cases are those where one person's exercise of autonomy would injure another person. It is quite right for there to be laws which prohibit people from firing airguns at others. The restriction on the autonomy of the shooters is minimal, and the pain they could cause to the others very large.

More problematic are cases where an individual's autonomy is likely to reduce his own pleasure, and the intervention would be paternalistic. It is one thing to say that we should be stopped from harming other people, but quite another to say that we should be stopped from acting against our own interests, *vide* Mill's liberty principle. However I think that most would agree it is sometimes justifiable to restrict a person's autonomy to prevent them from suffering great pain. If a human being is bitten by a rabid dog he will most likely contract rabies and die an extremely painful death, unless immediately given a course of (rather painful) injections through the navel. Suppose someone has been bitten but is unwilling to have the vaccinations because he fears the immediate pain of the injections more than the later pain of rabies. In these circumstances I think it would be entirely consistent with respect and caring for the patient to cajole him, and if necessary, force him to have the vaccinations in order to spare him later agony.

## Heteronomous choices

Although autonomy requires an agent to act according to her own choices, the mere fact that someone is choosing what to do does not make the choice autonomous. We have already considered the cases of Aegeus and Mill's incautious bridge crosser. Because each of these people would be acting in the light of crucially false beliefs, their actions would have been less than autonomous. All creatures with a will are autonomous in the same sense as we are all rational. However we are not perfectly autonomous any more than we are perfectly rational. Beliefs, desires or actions which are not fully rational are called 'irrational', even though they are all rational in the sense of being the product of some reasons (bad ones). Similarly actions which are the product of impaired choices are called 'heteronomous'.

Actions may be heteronomous either if they are the product of false beliefs, as in the case of Aegeus, or if they depend on irrational beliefs (whether or not the beliefs turn out to be true) or if they run counter to the agent's own assessment of what would be the best thing to do.

Here are two illustrative examples. Someone believes that she will contract skin cancer if she goes outside, and consequently always insists on staying at home. Her decision never to go out is heteronomous if it is irrational for her to believe that she will contract skin cancer if she goes out. Someone who cared about her might legitimately cajole her into going out, even though she does not want to, on the grounds that her decision to stay in is heteronomous, because grounded on an irrational belief.

The second example is of someone who acts against what he judges to be best overall. A partially reformed heroin addict both wants to give up his habit, and wants another fix when he is beset by withdrawal symptoms. He believes that the best thing for him to do is to withstand the immediate pain of the withdrawal symptoms so that he can conquer his addiction. Suppose that in spite of this he accepts another fix. If my description of him is correct, then this decision is heteronomous. The addict is not fully in control of himself.

In these circumstances it would be consistent with respect for his autonomy to help this person to do what he believes would be best, even though this was not what he would choose to do himself. Such an intervention could be justified by direct appeal to the value of autonomy.

### Autonomy vs. autonomy

The final set of circumstances in which it may be justifiable to stop someone from doing what she wants to do is where the intended action would itself damage someone's autonomy. The clearest cases are those where one person's intended action would undermine the autonomy of another. Even if I autonomously wanted to enslave another person I should not be allowed to do so, because this would seriously damage the other person's autonomy – even if I were a benign would-be slave owner.

The more difficult cases, once again, are those where a person's current exercise of autonomy would undermine his long-term autonomy. It sounds paradoxical to speak of paternalistically restricting an individual's *autonomous* actions out of concern for his *autonomy*. However in this case initial appearances are deceptive. Because people exist through time, so do their interests in autonomy. A present exercise of autonomy may damage one's future autonomy interests. An extreme case would be signing a contract to sell oneself into slavery (in a place where such contracts were enforceable). A person *could* autonomously sign such a contract. However such an act could ruin her long-term autonomy, and in these circumstances preventing her from taking this action, by guile or force if necessary, could be entirely consistent with a caring attitude of respect for her autonomy. Less dramatic but more common examples include decisions to try heroin, and signing up for terms in the armed forces.

**Autonomy and time**

I have claimed that there are two *paternalistic* grounds for sometimes interfering with a person's freedom of action – the protection of his interests in pleasure, and the protection of his autonomy. The first raises serious questions about how to calculate trade-offs between losses of autonomy and gains in pleasure. However my concern in the rest of this chapter is with the second ground – particularly where there is a reason to restrict a person's current autonomous actions out of respect for her own autonomy.

According to classical utilitarianism the right way to behave is to seek to maximise pleasure. Pleasure is regarded as the only intrinsic good, and in one's decision-making one should adopt an attitude of strict neutrality in respect of both people and time. This is because the fact that a pleasure is mine or yours does not in itself affect its value, nor are more distant pleasures or pains any less intrinsically good or bad than nearer ones.

One objection to classical msa utilitarianism is that it appears to regard people as of merely instrumental value – as the generators of the only intrinsically valuable material – pleasure. Antipaternalist objectors to msa utilitarianism cite the importance of respect for people's autonomy. But how should respect for someone's autonomy be manifested in light of the fact that sometimes autonomous decisions reduce a persons long-term autonomy?

One answer would be to adopt the extreme libertarian position of saying that, provided they do not harm anyone else, people should be able to make whatever autonomous choices they like – even choices which will adversely affect their autonomy interests throughout their life as a whole. If you really respect someone as an autonomous agent you will not prevent her from making her own life-affecting decisions, even if you realise these decisions will harm her in the long run. This is a view which appears to gain some support from a view expressed in Bernard Williams's influential paper (1976). Williams rejects those moralities which require one to dedicate one's life to the pursuit of neutral goals. First he attacks the requirement of interpersonal neutrality, by pointing out that there is a big difference between my relationship to some of my own projects and my relation to the projects of others. He claims that an emphasis on moral impartiality exaggerates the similarity between the two relationships:

> by providing ultimately too slim a sense in which any projects are mine at all. This point . . . involves the idea that my present projects are the condition of my existence, in the sense that unless I am propelled forward by the conatus of desire, project and interest, it is unclear why I should go on at all: the world, certainly, as a kingdom of moral agents, has no particular claim on my presence or, indeed, interest in it. (That kingdom, like others, has to respect the natural right to emigration.) (Williams, 1981, p. 12).

The suggestion is that if a person appears to be bound by an impartial concern for the projects of all humanity, this might reduce the point for him of continuing to exist, to such an extent that he might not want to continue at all. Certainly for most of us, in order for life to be worth living, we need to give special weight to our own personal projects, sometimes at the expense of neutral moral goals.

Williams then expresses the following view about neutrality in respect of time: 'the correct perspective on one's life is *from now*' (ibid. p. 13). This implies that, just as one should give special weight to *one's own* projects, so too one should give special weight to one's present projects. The same reason applies. Unless I give special weight to my present concerns, life may lose its lustre for me, and I might see no reason to continue living. Myself in the future is dependent for its existence on my deciding now to carry on living. Therefore it is proper that I should give special weight to my present concerns, even at the expense of myself in the future.

These arguments against neutrality derive their plausibility from the claim that the direct pursuit of substantive neutral goals, such as utility maximisation, is likely to be self-defeating, given human nature. We are constructed in such a way that the impartiality which is apparently required by these neutralist philosophies is completely unsatisfying for us. If we base all our individual decisions on judgments about whether or not they will best serve some concerns which we do not *now* have, the result is likely to be depression, ineffectiveness, and possibly suicide.

In the light of these considerations, should a member of the caring professions allow, and indeed encourage, her clients to do what is best from the clients' present perspective (provided it does not harm others), or should she seek to help the clients maximise their autonomy overall?

First it should be pointed out that Williams's argument against neutralism is not an argument against the acceptability of the neutralist *goals*, but rather an attack on the idea of individuals devoting their lives to the exclusive *direct* pursuit of such goals. In the case of my own autonomy, if I want to be maximally autonomous throughout my life, I should give special weight to my present concerns. The substantive goal of autonomy maximisation needs to be approached indirectly, not rejected altogether.

Secondly, even if it is true that complete neutrality would lead a person to think his life had no point, it does not follow that supreme weight should be given to his present concerns, but only sufficient weight to ensure that life does not become unutterably dreary in the way Williams warns us about.

There is no reason why someone in a caring profession should not, out of respect for his client, seek to maximise the client's autonomy overall. This is indeed a laudable goal. The implication of Williams's arguments for the caring professions is that social workers, teachers, doctors, nurses and other carers should be especially sensitive to the psychological damage which can be done to people through insufficient weight being given to their present perspective on the world. It by no means follows that this perspective should be accorded supreme weight. Indeed there are circumstances where a caring attitude would require that a present perspective be overruled - in the name of respect for autonomy.

If a person's autonomy is worth protecting because of autonomy's intrinsic value, it is not irrational to pursue a strategy whose ultimate goal is the maximisation of her autonomy. It is just that such a goal may not be *directly* achievable, and may require some special weight to be given to the person's present concerns. Here are two illustrative examples.

Dora is seventeen and very much wants to marry her boy friend now, settle down and have children. She is very much in love, but none the less realises that getting married now is likely to reduce her autonomy greatly over the years. She is even aware that she is likely to regret her early marriage in the years to come. Nevertheless this is what she most wants to do, and she does not now wish she did not want to marry.

We can say the following. It would probably be better for Dora if she did not want to marry now - certainly in regard to her autonomy chances. However, given that this *is* what she most wants, it might be worse for her to decide (inauthentically?) not to marry. It would likely be self-defeating for a carer (say a parent) to use coercive means to prevent the marriage. Unless the prospective husband really was a brute (in which case the daughter's decision to marry would most likely be heteronomous), respect for the daughter would lead one not to obstruct the marriage, and at most to argue against it.

Here is the other example. Bill, a married man of fifty with grown up children, has just been left for another by his wife. He is utterly despondent and has started to dabble in heroin. From his present perspective he just wants pleasant oblivion. His decision to take heroin is autonomous, in that it is not founded on false or irrational beliefs; nor is it contrary to what he judges to be the best, from his present point of view.

We can say the following about Bill. If he is able to survive the next twelve months without being driven to suicide or becoming a heroin addict it is likely that his acute despondency will abate, and that he will once again find an interest in life. On the other hand if he continues taking heroin and becomes addicted his long-term prospects for autonomy would be grim. In these circumstances it would be best for him, all things considered, if he were able to resist the desire to take heroin, and to survive the difficult twelve months or so without resort to such desperate measures. But he is unable, and unwilling to do so.

Let us now introduce John. John is a social worker who has been assigned to Bill, after Bill was convicted of being drunk and disorderly in a public place. John has, by chance, discovered that Bill has been taking heroin, although nobody knows that he knows (so if he does nothing he will not be in danger of being convicted of dereliction of duty). Should John be prepared, out of concern for Bill, to report him to the police and thereby coerce him into stopping taking heroin?

Just to report him, without discussing the matter with Bill first, would be inconsistent with respect for Bill, unless there was strong evidence that Bill might be driven to do something stupid by the conversation taking place. So if John were going to do anything he should talk to Bill, and thus place himself in possible danger if he were to do nothing further. Suppose the conversation took place, and it emerged that Bill really did want to seek pleasant oblivion through heroin. It might still be legitimate for John paternalistically to report Bill, in order to prevent Bill completely losing his autonomy. However this would be consistent with caring for Bill only if John did it because he believed that the help which Bill would be offered would actually be effective – not just in getting him off the drugs but also in helping him through the difficult period until such time as he had recovered some *joie de vivre*. It would be objectively right only if Bill's belief was correct.

### Conclusion

As stated earlier, this chapter lacks theoretical elegance. I hope that to some extent what it loses in elegance it gains in plausibility. Although philosophy can be helpful in clarifying the issues which lead to moral dilemmas, I do not believe that philosophical theory can remove the need for hard thinking and painful heart-searching which members of the caring professions often have to contend with in their work.

As far as paternalism is concerned, I hope to have shown that a belief that paternalistic intervention is sometimes justifiable, even in the lives of autonomous individuals, is not inconsistent with a genuine respect for people and a belief in the intrinsic value of autonomy. It does not follow that paternalism should pose no moral problem for carers. I suspect that professional carers are inclined to be paternalistic far more than would be justifiable on the view presented here. Indeed the dangers of misplaced paternalistic intervention are so great that there should be a strong presumption against treating clients paternalistically, except as a last resort – either to save the client from horrendous pain or to protect the client's overall autonomy.

## Note

I would like to thank Gavin and Susan Fairbairn for comments on an earlier draft.

## References

Dworkin, G. (1972), 'Paternalism', *The Monist*, vol. 56; repr. in Laslett and Fishkin, eds (1980), *Philosophy, Politics and Society*, 5th ser. Cambridge University Press.

Gert, B. and Culver, C. (1976), 'Paternalistic behavior', *Philosophy and Public Affairs*, vol. 6.

Gert, B. and Culver, C. (1982), *Philosophy in Medicine* Oxford University Press, ch. 7.

Glover, J. (1977), *Causing Death and Saving Lives*. Harmondsworth, Penguin.

Lindley, R. (1986), *Autonomy*. London, Macmillan.

Mill, J. S. (1859), *On Liberty*. Quotations from Dent edn. (1976), *Utilitarianism, On Liberty and Representative Government*.

Williams, B. (1976), 'Persons, character and morality', repr. in id. (1981), *Moral Luck*. Cambridge University Press.

# 7 Respecting feelings

*James Brown*

This chapter is prompted in part by a talk at the 1984 Ethical Issues in Caring conference in Manchester, on the experiences of women who had miscarriages or whose babies died perinatally. It is written with cases of that kind very much in mind. But I hope that such interest as it has extends to caring in general inasmuch as those involved in caring have to take account of the feelings of those they care for.

## Caring and feelings

Ethics is about how persons should conduct themselves, especially in their encounters and interactions with other persons. One might take the following tough-minded view of medical ethics. Doctors have a job to do. When a person is in pain or discomfort or is unable to function normally through some disorder or disability, the doctor's job is to find out what is wrong, to find a way of restoring normality or improving the situation and to see that steps are taken to implement that way. She has, to be sure, a moral duty to do this job to the best of her ability (within reason), and to maintain her ability. But she has no special moral responsibilities beyond those of maintaining competence and efficiency. There is no more to medical ethics than to plumbing ethics or bus-driving ethics. One could take a similarly tough-minded view of nursing ethics. A nurse has a job to do. A nurse is a medical auxiliary and has the task of implementing the doctor's plan for improvement or restoration. Like a doctor or plumber, a nurse has a responsibility to maintain competence and efficiency. There is no more to nursing ethics than that.

One might go further in this tough-minded direction and maintain that the idea of a nursing ethics going beyond that minimum is positively harmful. Consider for a moment a minimalist view of the state. Starting from such a view one might go on to argue that giving the state other functions in addition to its proper ones is harmful and leads to a situation in which not even the proper function of the state is adequately discharged. Thus one might maintain that the state is nothing but an arrangement whereby the transactions and agreements entered into by individuals are to be protected from interference, and the parties to these transactions and agreements are to be protected from unfair practices; and one might argue that attributing more extensive duties and responsibilities to the state leads to a bloated state and a corrupted and unhealthy society. Analogously one might maintain that nursing is nothing but assistance and labour for doctoring; and one might argue that assigning more extensive responsibilities to the nursing role leads to the proper function of nursing becoming obscured and hence to the medical task being less well carried out. In particular, it might be argued, the idea that nursing should be professional caring is a pernicious idea and may even be an incoherent one.

One way to resist this tough-minded line of thought would be to develop a convincing account of professional caring and what it involves. In the following I make an attempt at contributing to such an account. My hope is that through the gradual building up of a convincing account of the things involved in professional caring it will be increasingly possible for tough-minded criticism to be resisted.

In her book *Beast and Man*, Mary Midgley has argued against regarding the affective side of our nature as a dispensable extra bit that just happens to be there and might well not have been.

> We cannot dismiss our emotions and the rest of our nonintellectual nature, along with the body and the earth it is fitted for, as alien, contingent stuff. We have somehow to operate as a whole, to preserve the continuity of our being.[1]

If this is correct it holds equally in our dealings with others. Caring for people cannot consist in treating them just as one would treat bits of machinery that need repairing. In the same book Midgley has emphasised that '*caring for* people means serving their needs as well as wanting to be near them', and relatedly, 'thinking highly of them'.[2] Another writer, Nel Noddings, cites the philosopher and theologian Martin Buber and clearly thinks of a complete caring relationship as being an I-thou relationship; one feature of this is that if I am relating to you in an I-thou way, then I cannot disregard something's mattering to you, worrying you, delighting you, and so on.[3]

The focus of this chapter is on aspects of professional caring that have to do with the feelings of the recipient of care. I shall suggest that care of a person involves having regard for the person's feelings; that having regard for a person's feelings involves different things in the cases of two different classes of feelings, it involves respecting some feelings and not others; and that being good at caring for people involves being able to tell reasonably well which feelings are to be respected and which are not. If this is even roughly correct, then nothing like the tough-minded story will do.

We should do no harm to those in our care. That, I assume, is clear and uncontroversial. And doing no harm presumably includes causing no needless pain or distress. Suppose a person is so constituted that in certain avoidable circumstances he or she is likely to feel pain. (It may be that a particular mechanical toy is liable to give a child a painful pinch.) Then caring for that person includes taking steps to avert that pain. Now suppose that the person is so constituted as to be liable to have feelings of shock, terror, anxiety, revulsion and so on, in certain avoidable circumstances. Then caring for that person includes taking steps, where necessary, to avert such experiences or – if they occur – to shorten or alleviate them. Moreover suppose there is something from which a person derives feelings of satisfaction; it might be a TV programme or the view from a particular window or a cooperative response to an oft-repeated joke question. Then helping to bring those feelings about can be part of caring for that person. These kinds of considerate behaviour with regard to a person's feelings I propose to call *appeasing* those feelings.[4]

It thus appears that appeasing a person's feelings (unless there is good reason for not appeasing them) is part of the business of caring. I want to suggest that respecting a person's feelings is another part of the business of caring. My aim is to state and amplify the following point: some of a person's feelings are reflections of what that person sets store by or attaches importance to, and others are not; respecting a person in the context of caring involves paying due attention to this difference and having regard for what matters to the person.

**Appeasement and respect**
Some feelings are to be respected while others are to be coped with in other ways – making them stop occurring, avoiding the situations in which they occur, giving treatment to reduce their duration or intensity when they do occur. Appeasing feelings can be done without the feelings being respected at all. A person may procure a fix for a drug addict in order to alleviate the addict's distress without having any respect for the addict's felt need for drugs. Likewise one may avoid contentious subjects when talking to an ageing racist in order to avoid causing him or her distress, and yet have no respect at all for the racist sentiments. Such respect as one has for these persons might be in spite of those feelings rather than such as to lead to respect for the feelings. It must be acknowledged that appeasing a person's feelings (except, presumably, where doing so is destructive of the person) can be a way of reminding or assuring the person that he or she matters. But even then appeasing feelings is not yet respecting feelings.[5]

Suppose a man in hospital has feelings of anxiety which are due to false beliefs about his diagnosis. In that case removing the beliefs might well alleviate the feelings. Now consider the feelings which accompany a person's bereavement. It might be suggested that the feelings are due to the belief that someone is dead, and that we could aim to alleviate the feelings by removing the belief. But consider the mother of a beloved ten-year-old accident victim who comes to have the delusion that her child is still alive after all. If anything, we sorrow for her even more when she is deluded than when she is not. This shows that removing the cause of feelings of bereavement is not an appropriate aim in caring for the bereaved. These feelings are thus of a radically different kind from headaches, for example, where aiming to remove the cause is entirely appropriate.

If we are not to remove the cause in belief, perhaps a suitable aim would be the removal of the feelings and even their replacement by feelings of elation. But a moment's thought should satisfy us that this too is not something to aim for. A parent who in all sincerity claims to be *glad* about a beloved and happy child's sudden accidental death summons up pity in us just as the parent who will not believe the child is dead does. A parent's feelings being simply unaffected by their child's death would also evoke worry or alarm.

So, although the feelings experienced by a person who is bereaved are unpleasant, getting rid of them – or at any rate getting rid of them too quickly – is not an aim of caring.[6] Why is this? It is surely because the feelings are the appropriate ones; the person really has suffered a dreadful loss, what has happened really does matter, and the feelings are a reflection of its mattering. The bereaved person is respected as is that person's affective acknowledgement of bereavement. The feelings are respected in that they are accepted for what they are, they are not denied, trivialised, reinterpreted or removed. They are also confirmed by the condolences of others.[7]

The situation is different where someone has groundless feelings of bereavement. Then the feelings are real enough but there is no death of a person to which they relate. If the feelings arise in connection with false or misleading information, then removal of the feelings by correcting the information is entirely the right thing to aim for. If the feelings are associated with an insane conviction that someone has died (a conviction which has perhaps resulted from the feelings themselves or from an attempt to provide a rationale for them), then psychiatric treatment is appropriate. There is no question here of the feelings being respected.

## Some feelings to appease and some to respect
I give here a few examples to make plainer to the reader what the contrast between feelings that are to be respected and feelings that are to be appeased is supposed to amount to.

A man might, without warning, find in himself a revulsion – a rising of the gorge – on having a plate of oysters placed before him. Or suppose a person has a pathological aversion to snakes, worms and things that look similar to them. It is not that the person has something against snakes, thinks they are dirty, dangerous, or anything like that. Here, while there are recurrent feelings about something, a snake-free environment is not something which the person sets store by. Given the feelings, the person of course prefers to be in a snake-free environment. But the person would be just as content for the aversion to disappear. It is not something to be respected. To be sure, consideration for the person does require that (except perhaps as part of treatment for the phobia) one does not needlessly place them among snakes or pictures of snakes or in the hospital bed next to a snake-lover. The aversions against oysters and snakes are feelings which are to be appeased rather than respected.

In July 1983 there was a television programme about the reporting of war in the newspapers. In this programme a newspaper correspondent admitted playing down the more horrific side of the Falklands conflict. In particular, after the Bluff Cove incident he did not send back copy about the mutilated bodies, the jumble of limbs, and so on. This was in part because he had known some of the men quite well; he said that writing about the bodies in an impersonal way did not feel fair. This feeling is one which is to be respected rather than appeased (if it is to be thought of as a feeling at all).

Again many of us know parts of the world where it upsets people to know that the Sabbath is being violated and where one way of violating the Sabbath is to wash your car on a Sunday morning. Consider someone who does not feel any religious obligation to refrain from washing the car but whose neighbours would be upset by it. Suppose further that the neighbours are not at all vindictive: they are not going to forbid their children to play with the car-washer's children, they are not going to behave discourteously or retaliate in any other way. The would-be car-washer has nothing at all to lose by washing the car. Nevertheless he may decide to leave it dirty (or wash it at a more inconvenient time the day before) solely because of the neighbours' religious feelings. It is not that he wants to spare the neighbours the unpleasant experience of getting angry or sorrowful; rather it is the disrespect involved in giving offence that he wishes to avoid. I want to suggest that he is not being irrational in treating the neighbours' feelings as a reason for abstaining from washing the car.

Now comes my principal example. At the 1984 EIC conference one of the speakers made us very much aware of the plight of women in cases of stillbirth or perinatal death; in such cases the woman is often treated to breezy assurances that she is young and healthy and capable of having lots more children,[8] or is just treated as depressed and given antidepressant drugs. What the woman is not permitted to do is *grieve*, *mourn* and be treated as *bereaved*. For a woman in this situation there is a massive discrepancy between the way she feels and the way others behave towards her and permit her to behave.[9] Her feelings are not acknowledged for what they are but are either disregarded or treated as something different. This discrepancy or disharmony between the way the woman feels and the way others behave towards her is a problem. It seems to me that the correct solution to this problem consists in the woman's feelings being respected. Her feelings, like those of the journalist and the strict Sabbatarian neighbours, are to be respected, whereas the feelings about snakes and oysters are only to be appeased.

## Why to strive for respect in the central case

Someone who naturally and fully shares the grieving feelings of a woman who has miscarried will also respect those feelings. But should those for whom this respect does not come naturally strive for it? Noddings refers to 'a realization that the other – who feels intensely about that which I do not believe – is still one to be received'. And she continues, 'Watching another in prayer, or at communion, or even brandishing a holy sword, I may feel what he feels even though I reject what he believes. Then I am reconnected to this other in basic caring.'[10] Earlier in the book she says this:

> It may well be that you care deeply for some plant, animal, or environment in which I have no interest. My carelessness may shock and offend you. Now my obligation as one-caring is to listen, to receive you in all your indignation. I do not give way because of political pressure and the might of your lobbying, but I listen carefully because you address me. What matters to you is of interest and concern to me.[11]

We can respect the feelings of the journalist and of the strict Sabbatarians in something like this spirit. Even if we do not share those feelings our concern not to be contemptuous of the person is, in an understandable way, reason not to be contemptuous of those feelings.

But the feelings of a person with delusions of bereavement are still for treating rather than respecting. And we have yet to find convincing grounds for respecting the feelings of the woman who feels bereaved by miscarriage or perinatal death.

Let us look at that case again. A woman has given birth to a still-born child. She grieves. She has feelings of bereavement. Perhaps there is no person who has died. After all, the baby in her womb never told her a new joke or surprised her by confiding a secret worry. She had no interpersonal relationship with that baby. Unilateral feelings of tenderness are not enough to constitute an interpersonal relationship. It is true that there might have been a living person and there actually is not that person. But that does not seem to be enough to warrant mourning.

Suppose we say that there simply is no ground for bereavement-feelings (as opposed to treatable malaise, depression, and so on). If that is correct the feelings are associated with a false belief. Suppose this is explicitly recognised ('I'm afraid this unfortunate patient thinks she is bereaved'). Then an appropriate step is to point out to the woman that no person has died. The baby had not even begun to be a person, to develop a capacity to relate as a person to other persons. It was, to be sure, genetically unique, but as far as personality is concerned it was no different from any other unborn baby; in particular it was no different from other babies that this woman can confidently expect to have in future.

Perhaps a case can be made for tentatively and sensitively making these points to the woman. But the chances are that it will not do much good. And if health workers take up a stand on these points, then we are back with the problem that we started with, that is, the discrepancy between the woman's feelings and the response of the people around her. Insisting on the woman's acknowledging that bereavement cannot be what she is suffering from is no move towards solving the problem but rather helps to sustain and entrench it. So what is the next move to be?

Well, if someone is deluded and we have good reason not to keep on at them about their mistaken belief, then an appropriate policy may be a two-part policy of minimising distress and, as far as possible, bringing the patient back to acknowledgement of the same reality that those around them live in. Since doing the latter in the normal way – that is, by telling them – has now been ruled out, this bringing them back to normality has to be attempted by means of treatment. But once again this will be a sustaining of the problem and not a move towards solving it. For the person's feelings are being approached as headaches or nausea or a broken arm might be; they are not being responded to as *bereavement*. So we are back with the problem that the woman's experience is not being allowed to stand as it is but is reinterpreted in a way that she cannot accept.

Perhaps an appropriate way to deal with this problem is to pretend to share the woman's interpretation of her feelings. In other words, perhaps she should be humoured. If health workers are reasonably good at this the pretence may escape the patient's notice. But going in for a deception of this kind is an admission of defeat for any health worker who is endeavouring to respect the patient.[12] A course of this kind commends itself only in the absence of an acceptable alternative. So we need to consider whether there is an alternative.

Here I want to stress that the appropriateness of the feelings of bereavement is part of what is at issue. So it will not do simply to say that the woman is deluded and should be treated as such. Of course, if stillbirths and the deaths of newborns were regularly accompanied by general dementia, treating the woman as deluded would be appropriate. But they are not; and in the absence of other symptoms of psychiatric disorder in the individual case it would be viciously question-begging to regard persistence in feeling and behaving as though bereaved as evidence of temporary insanity. Moreover in caring, as in social science, it is good practice (in the absence of strong reasons for doing otherwise) to attribute to persons only such mental states as they can agree in ascribing to themselves.

Where does this leave us? We have been considering a line of thought that might be summarised like this: since the woman persists in having a belief that we cannot share, we are to appease her feelings with the kindness that we accord to silly people in our care. What we have seen however is that to reason this way would not be to respect the woman, for respecting her rules out treating her as just silly. So instead we are to reason that, since respecting her rules out treating her as just silly, her feelings of bereavement are to be respected and not just treated or appeased. The upshot is this: given the woman's self-ascription of feelings practically the same as feelings of bereavement, given the persistence of those feelings (perhaps despite its being tentatively put to the woman that hers is not really a case of bereavement since the dead baby was never a person), and given the absence of good independent reason to regard the woman as psychiatrically disordered, we have good reason to respond to that woman in ways that would be appropriate if we shared her view of the state of affairs. In short, I have tried to show that the bereavement feelings have to be respected, even by those who think that no person has died, because there is no acceptable way for them to be merely appeased.

It seems to me that respecting these feelings is akin to respecting people's religious beliefs, and also akin to not gratuitously wasting food at a time of famine even if the famine is remote: in each case we are not to show contempt for people by behaving contemptuously towards what is important to them.

## Which feelings to respect

I have suggested that caring for a person involves respecting some of that person's feelings and endeavouring to appease others. We now have to face the question, which feelings are to be respected and which merely appeased?

It would be convenient if the answer to this question was that the feelings which are to be respected are the ones we share. For feelings we share are the ones we can most easily take seriously and acknowledge for what they are, and which we are least inclined to dismiss as just silly or self-indulgent. But this answer would leave our main problem largely intact; the problem arose because patients had feelings not shared by those reponsible for treatment and care.

A second answer might be that the feelings to be respected are the intense ones. But this is not right either. A person's devotion to a spouse of many years standing or devotion to a cause or attachment to a place may be reflected in feelings of rather low intensity, while the same person may be intensely irritated by buses not stopping at bus stops or may have an intense revulsion against other people's children's runny noses. Intensity of feeling is a poor guide to the importance that a person takes things to have.

The correct answer, it seems to me, is that those feelings have a claim to be respected which reflect the person's setting store by something or seeing something as important. Now these might not be the most intense feelings the person has. They are rather those with which the person identifies or which are closely integrated into the person's self.[13] A person's daily life features a host of feelings, wants, desires, aversions, recognitions, surprises, rememberings, ideas, thoughts, plans, decisions, hesitations, actions, and so on. The individual normally comes to have characteristic responses to things and characteristic habits or regular patterns of feeling, thought and action. Some of these aspects of a person's life will be highly integrated with one another, coming to form the person's character or self. To the extent that an individual does something or has an impulse or feeling that is not closely integrated with the rest, the act or impulse or feeling is less readily attributable to the person. The present relevance of this is that where a feeling is comparatively unintegrated into the self of the person whose feeling it is, there is correspondingly little tendency for respecting the person to involve respecting the feeling. The sudden revulsion against oysters and the stubborn aversion to snakes are not integrated into the fabric of a person's self.[14] To the extent that their possessor can be distressed by them, they may call for some attention, but only for appeasement, not for respect. At the limit unintegrated feelings are ones that cannot be respected; for they lack the required relation to the person whose feelings they are – they are not a reflection of something that is important for the person or which the person sets store by, they are not an integral part of that person's sense of himself or herself.[15] Those feelings that are central to a person's life and are core components of herself are the ones that are most to be respected – unless there are good positive reasons for not respecting them. The feelings are to be respected, if at all, because the person is to be respected.[16]

Now recall the journalist who, after Bluff Cove, said that writing about the bodies in an impersonal way did not feel fair. Perhaps the idiom of feeling was not the appropriate one to use in this context. It creates a sense of self-deprecation, as when someone tells us about a strange unaccountable revulsion against doing something (like a revulsion against oysters). This feeling of revulsion is not at all the same kind of thing as the journalist's sense that sending in a description of the bodies would not be right. But let us grant that the journalist's awareness is a feeling. We still have to say that it is a very different kind of feeling from the revulsion against the oysters. It is intimately bound up with other aspects of the journalist's life: his relationship with the men when they were still alive, his respect for them, his self-respect, his choice of how to live his life (good copy at all costs?) and so on. The journalist's feeling about Bluff Cove reflects something of what he sets store by and regards as important, whereas (on the face of it) a feeling of revulsion against oysters does not.

The point about the feelings of a woman whose child was still-born is that they are often feelings of bereavement. In bereavement treatment which is aimed at simply the removal of oppressive feeling is misguided. The feelings have to do with someone being dead who might not have been dead. Short of bringing the deceased back to life, removing the cause of the feelings is not appropriate. Part of what is wrong with denying the feelings, trying to jolly the person out of them, or trying to focus remedial treatment on them, is that the feelings are too tightly integrated into the self for any of those courses to work.

Let me mention, in conclusion, something else that an emphasis on the integration of feelings throws light on. A point made in the *Guardian* article cited earlier is this: 'In some ways the more abstract early miscarriage can be *harder* to cope with – there is nothing on which to focus one's grief'.[17] To the extent that the attention of carers is drawn not only to the external events but also to the centrality of the bereavement feelings in the woman's self, the absence of an external focus for those feelings may not make the carers disposed to respect the feelings less.

## Notes

This is a modified version of a paper read at the 1985 EIC conference. Some material which was omitted at the conference to save time has been restored. For comments on different versions I am grateful to participants at the conference who joined in the discussion, to two colleagues at Coleraine, Dr T. J. McKnight and Miss P. Ashworth, and to Gavin Fairbairn.

1   Mary Midgley (1980), *Beast and Man* (London, Methuen), p. 196.
2   ibid. p. 340
3   Nel Noddings (1984), *Caring* (London, University of California Press), esp. ch. 3.

Both Midgley and Noddings indicate reservations about the idea of professional caring (see *Beast and Man*, p. 340n, and *Caring*, pp. 66–7). I do not attempt to discuss this aspect of our problem area.

4   Some readers may prefer to talk of appeasing persons rather than of appeasing feelings. I would then ask them to accept talk of appeasing certain feelings of a person as elliptical for talk of appeasing that person as far as those feelings are concerned.

5   You may show a person that (in your judgment) she is important by treating a whim of hers as if it were important. But it might not work; the disproportion between the importance it has and the importance that you treat it as having can be embarrassing to her.

6   '... how often do we read in a newspaper account that someone who has been thrown into deep shock by some traumatic incident, say the loss of her children in a fire, has been put under heavy sedation? To the doctors this may seem like the only proper, compassionate course of action, and maybe for some people it is; for others, however, dulling the agony now may only drive the grief inwards so deeply that the bereaved person never fully recovers' (Carolyn Faulder (1985), *Whose Body Is It?* (London, Virago), p. 28).

7   'These are seen as a tribute to the dead, thereby confirming the mourner in the belief that the dead person is worth all the pain' (Colin Murray Parkes (1975), *Bereavement* (Harmondsworth, Penguin), pp. 191–2).

8   A woman can find solace in this knowledge. See Ann Oakley, Dr Ann McPherson and Helen Roberts (1984), *Miscarriage* (Glasgow, Fontana), pp. 106–9. But in general, 'Clichés about being young enough to have another' are 'not at all helpful' (ibid. p. 123).

9   An article in the *Guardian*, 6 August 1985, mentions 'women who had had just one ordinary, early miscarriage and who had resorted to pretending that it happened later than it did, in order to justify their grief, which otherwise seemed excessive'.

10  Noddings, op. cit. p. 186.

11  ibid. p. 161.

12  See Sissela Bok (1980), *Lying* (London, Quartet), pp. 31, 238–41.

13  See Harry Frankfurt, Gary Watson and Charles Taylor (1982) in Gary Watson, ed., *Free Will*. Oxford University Press.

14  'Consider the case of a woman who has a sudden urge to drown her bawling child in the bath; or the case of a squash player who, while suffering an ignominious defeat, desires to smash his opponent in the face with the racquet. It is just false that the mother values her child's being drowned or that the player values the injury and suffering of his opponent. But they desire these things none the less. They desire them in spite of themselves' (Gary Watson in ibid. pp. 100–1). He goes on to argue that a person could 'be similarly estranged from a rather persistent and pervasive desire'. Appeasement in cases such as these, to be acceptable, would have to involve harmless outlets, cooling-off arrangements or other things of that sort.

15  'By integration I mean having a character, acting as a whole, having a firm and effective priority system...integration alone is something of enormous value, and respect seems a suitable name for the recognition with which we salute it' (Midgley, op. cit. p. 262).

16  However this has the corollary that, where it is impossible to respect central feelings, the person cannot be respected either. It may be that what a person sets store by is repugnant to one in such a way that one would feel soiled by anything that could be construed as acquiescence in the person's having those values. How a satisfactory account of professional caring is to do justice to this point I do not yet know.

17  cf. Oakley *et al.*, *Miscarriage*, op. cit. p. 123.

# 8   Ethical confrontation in counselling

*Brian Thorne*

In 1979 I contributed an article to the journal *Theology* in which I attempted to tease out some of the complex issues surrounding the themes of guilt and conscience (Thorne, 1979). The article was prompted by my experience as a counsellor working in the person-centred tradition of Carl Rogers and by my struggle to make sense of the Christian contribution to these issues. Not long ago I was counselling a student who was shortly to leave the University of East Anglia and during the session I almost came to believe that she was consciously presenting me with a textbook illustration of my own theories. I should like to say something about that counselling session: it will serve as a useful summary of my previously expounded ideas and will also form a springboard for the further reflections I now wish to make.

The client in question (I shall call her Margaret) was exploring the many difficulties which would confront her at the end of the term when she would cease to be a member of the university. Chief among these difficulties was her fear of returning to live once more with her family. Her parents, whom she loved, were worthy people much given to good works and with a strong sense of their own values and what constitutes a worthwhile life. Margaret experienced them as powerful and influential and she found it painfully difficult to question their view of reality and their firmly held, if often unspoken, convictions about life and how it should be lived. As a result she found that after a couple of days in the parental home she felt stifled and oppressed. What is more she began to feel guilty and confused. It became clear during our counselling session that Margaret had to avoid living at home after graduation if she was to have any chance of hanging on to her own identity and developing as the person she wanted to be. As this realisation became increasingly focused Margaret came out with the following statement: 'If I don't try and live away from home I shall be going against my conscience.' At this point I let out an inward cheer of delight for here was a client who was using the word 'conscience' to denote the faculty which enables a person to keep in touch with the meaning and significance of his or her life and to discover what course of action is in accord with that meaning. It is my contention that this is indeed the true conscience and that failure to listen to it will evoke an *appropriate* form of guilt – namely that profound dissatisfaction at having failed to live and act in accordance with the meaning and potential of one's own unique life and identity. Such guilt is useful and even desirable in so far as it can aid a person in the search for wholeness and fulfilment. It is the guilt which springs from attentiveness to the true conscience which, in Cardinal Newman's marvellous words, speaks as 'the voice of God in the nature and heart of man'.

You will remember though, that when Margaret was at home she quickly became guilty and confused. The guilt she experienced in that setting has nothing to do with the *appropriate* guilt I have described. Rather it was the feeling of being somehow unworthy and delinquent in the eyes of her parents whose values and view of reality she found herself defenceless to resist, having presumably been conditioned by them for most of her life. Her confusion was the result of the rapid slipping away of her own sense of identity once she was plunged back into the parental home. In a disturbing and frightening way she quickly lost herself and began confusedly to assume again the personality her parents would have wished her to have. The guilt she then experienced was the *inappropriate* guilt which ensnares us when we have failed to live up to someone else's view of how we should live and act. This guilt tells us nothing about the meaning and potential of our own unique existence: on the contrary it conceals such meaning from us and condemns us to an alienated existence in which we attempt to live out a destiny which is not ours and in all probability brings in its wake sickness both of soul and body and often of mind as well. Furthermore the internal voice which provokes this inappropriate guilt is *not*, I would submit, the voice of conscience at all. It is rather the internalised prompting of an external authority, whether this be parents, boss, church, government or the writings of Karl Marx or the Hebrew prophets. This is not to suggest that the true conscience and the internalised prompting of an external authority cannot speak the same message simultaneously. Of course they can and such unison does occur. Unfortunately however it is my experience that all too often they do *not* speak the same message or even the same language. What is more the internalised external authority is frequently so strident in its dogmatic demands that the true conscience cannot be heard at all except perhaps as a faint whisper when inappropriate guilt relaxes its feverish grip for a fleeting moment.

For those of us in the helping professions I believe that one of our most formidable and yet essential tasks is to create an environment where such fleeting moments can occur and then to assist our clients to be attentive to this faint whisper which is the attempt of the true conscience to make itself heard. Such a task demands infinite patience and delicacy. It also demands that we are not ourselves living out alienated lives, mere puppets jerking frenetically on the strings of an external authority in a vain attempt to keep our own inappropriate guilt at bay. How sad it is to come across those helpers – sometimes in prestigious professional positions – who care for others not because that is the meaning of their lives but because not to do so would release such a flood of inappropriate guilt that life for them would scarcely be tolerable. They are not only painfully out of touch with the core of their own being but they are a danger to those they feel compelled to help. Full of inappropriate guilt themselves they are likely to exacerbate a similar guilt in their clients.

I wish to explore further the task of creating an environment in which the true conscience can make itself heard. I have said that such a task demands infinite patience and delicacy, and so it does for it involves most importantly the offering of a deeply felt acceptance whose unconditionality communicates itself to the very heart of the person in need. There must be an utter absence of judgment and a deep faith in the other person's capacity and desire to move towards the good. Such an environment is not created overnight: often it needs months or even years of consistent and unconditional acceptance before the first whisper of the true conscience can make itself heard. Such waiting is a great test for the helper and it will sometimes drive him to the limits of his patience. In this respect it is important to remember that many of those who are most alienated from themselves and are in the deepest distress have lived for many years in an environment where they feel judged and found wanting every minute of the day. It is not therefore surprising that it sometimes takes an unconscionable time for unconditional acceptance to be recognised for what it is, let alone for it to be experienced as a real and liberating response from one human being to another. Mother Julian of Norwich would have it that the helper shares in the parenthood of God as he offers unconditional acceptance to his client, and that is saying something very big indeed.

If the truth be known most of us *expect* to be adversely judged by others and we spend a great deal of time and effort trying to win favourable judgment. Even the delinquent is following the same pattern for he seeks to win the favourable judgment of his peer group by ensuring that he earns the condemnation of those authorities he hates or despises. For most of us it is, I believe, a rare experience to feel unconditionally accepted. When it happens to me I notice that an almost predictable process occurs. At first I feel hesitant and disbelieving – I can hardly credit my good fortune. I test it out probably by trying to shock or provoke a little. When the moment arrives that confirms me in my hope I sense a great relaxation which permeates every fibre of my being. I often feel sleepy and sometimes there is a faint urge to curl up in the other person's arms. I rest awhile and then there comes flooding in a wave of new energy. I feel creative and excited. I can think and feel with clarity and intensity. I do not have to worry if I appear powerful or weak, virtuous or scandalous. I am alive and on the move towards the meaning of my life. My true conscience speaks to me and I might even find the courage to obey its promptings. If I do I shall almost certainly have whiffs of inappropriate guilt or even a cloud of it and shall have to struggle to remind myself that I do not accept the jurisdiction of the court into which I have allowed myself misguidedly to wander. On the worst occasions obeying my true conscience seems to involve a determined effort on my part not to heed a furious judge with a red face who suddenly jumps into my path and would have me locked up.

One of the saddest discoveries I have made during my fifteen years as a professional counsellor is that for many of my clients this furious judge comes masquerading as God himself. The sequence of events in such cases goes something like this. The distressed person comes full of pain, guilt and deeply self-rejecting. If I am lucky a relationship gradually develops in which I attempt to offer those conditions for therapeutic change which Carl Rogers elucidated long ago – unconditional acceptance, empathic understanding and my own genuineness. The feelings of guilt become increasingly susceptible to exploration as the client gradually relaxes and becomes less self-rejecting. In most cases the guilt can be traced back to the failure to live out parental wishes or to come up to the expectations of significant others. There is then a period of agonising confusion as the client seeks to struggle free of the powerful but inappropriate guilt feelings without as yet being able to hear the voice of true conscience and without therefore having any sense of direction. Constantly there is the urge to return to the known prison of guilt and self-rejection: the familiar cell seems preferable to the unknown and frightening world of freedom. The day comes at last when the first whisperings of true conscience are heard. The client experiences the first ineffable feelings of self-love and senses that he yearns for the good and the true. It is a precious moment which is sometimes almost overwhelming in its intensity.

At this point I rejoice with my client that he has found himself, recognised his own value and is now in a position to offer himself to life. But then comes the most agonising part of the whole process. The next time the client arrives he is full of despair, confusion and anger. He looks at me as if I have taken on satanic characteristics. He has met the red-faced furious judge whom he identifies as God and at a stroke I am cast in the role of Lucifer to whom he has all but lost his soul. The words of the furious judge come through loud and clear: 'Have you forgotten all you have ever learned? Have you not heard of the sin of egotism?

How dare you spend so much time dwelling on your own absurd feelings. Have you forgotten that you are a worm and no man? Have you forgotten that without me you are nothing – I could extinguish you with a flick of my fingers. How dare you inflate your self-importance. Cross out the I and take up your cross. Be concerned for others, abhor this appalling me-worship. You are on the point of falling into the clutches of a guru of the me-generation which has forgotten all about sacrifice, constraint and renunciation. One step further and you are lost.'

What is perhaps astonishing is that clients who have no religious allegiance are almost as likely to meet this furious judge as the practising Christian who is plunged back at this stage into a whole system of Christian education and training which is based essentially on anxiety and fear and a lack of confidence in human nature. It would seem that the condemnatory God of the neurotic Church is rampant still in the unconscious realm of secular man.

It is not easy to endure the experience of being perceived as satanic and there are times, I confess, when it seems easier to give up the struggle and to leave the client in a far more glorious prison than the one he inhabited before calling upon my help. Perhaps after all it is a perverse therapeutic triumph to have enabled a client to reach the top-notch prison where God himself is the governor – much better than the grimy provincial gaol staffed by parents, schoolteachers or the faceless purveyors of society's norms.

It will be clear from my preoccupation with conscience, guilt and judgment that I perceive many of my clients as caught in the grips of the most furious ethical conflicts where oughts and wants struggle desperately for some kind of inner harmony. And yet prior to the moment when I am suddenly cast in the role of Lucifer, the bringer of false light, it is unlikely that I shall have experienced any desire to confront my client in the ethical arena. On the contrary, as I have stressed, it is highly probable that I shall have bent over backwards to refrain from such confrontation. It is only too evident to me that many of those who seek counselling help have had numerous judges in their lives already without my being added to the list. Indeed both Freud and Rogers, despite very different concepts of human nature, identify moralism as the root of much psychic disorder. Furthermore it is possible to encapsulate much of what I have already said by stating the belief (which I certainly hold) that the healing of neuroses is dependent upon the creation of a non-moralistic relationship in which a person can experience that his worth as a human being is without conditions.

Up to the Lucifer moment too, although my patience and my faith may have been sorely taxed, nothing has happened to disturb profoundly my optimistic view that, given the right conditions, a person will develop in self-enhancing ways and in a manner which will advance the common good. Nothing too has made me doubt to any serious degree my belief that my client has the right and the capacity for self-direction and does not stand in need of my guidance whether this be overt or covert. Moral non-intervention has been a logical outcome of my positive view of man and of my understanding of the therapeutic process.

Now however, as I experience my client's rejection of me and of the process to which I have attached such value, I find myself shaken to the foundations. I seem to be witnessing the most shocking act of self-betrayal on my client's part. He has found himself, only to be overcome with such fear and dismay that he is now striving to lose himself again as quickly as possible. What am I to do? If I value my client's freedom so highly must I not allow him to be free to reject me and the healing process itself? Does not my own value system require me to extend to my client the liberty to choose the prison of his neurosis rather than the freedom of unconditional self-regard? If I turn to Carl Rogers I receive what seems a plain enough answer. Rogers speaks of the therapeutic process and its outcomes in these words:

> But is the therapist willing to give the client the full freedom as to outcomes? Is he genuinely willing for the client to organise and direct his life? Is he willing for him to choose goals that are social or anti-social, moral or immoral? If not, it seems doubtful that therapy will be a profound experience for the client. Even more difficult, is he willing for the client to choose regression rather than growth or maturity? to choose neuroticism rather than mental health? to choose to reject help rather than accept it? to choose death rather than life? (Rogers, 1965)

The implication of all this is evident. According to Rogers the counsellor should indeed honour his client's freedom to choose death and destruction if that is how he so decides. Not to do so would be a kind of denial of the rationale of the therapeutic process. It is but a short step from this position to a stance which sees ethical confrontation or moral intervention as inevitably in conflict with the therapeutic efficacy of unconditional acceptance. Using different language Freud arrives at much the same conclusion. The analyst too is forbidden to play the part of mentor. The patient must be free to select what he will and the therapist's 'conscience is not burdened whatever the outcome' (Freud, 1949).

I must confess to an increasing uneasiness with both Rogers and Freud on this issue, an uneasiness which now threatens to bubble over into rebellion. I am utterly certain that my own right to exist does not depend upon my client choosing goodness and wholeness, but that is a very different matter to adopting a posture of silence or neutrality at the very moment when my client faces the choice of life and good or death and evil. I can no longer rest comfortably with the notion that therapeutic necessity demands that I display a kind of ethical emptiness in the face of my client's fear of freedom. Indeed I am rapidly approaching a contrary point of view and yet, as I do so, I like to feel that I am not deviating essentially from the person-centred approach which characterises all that I undertake as a counsellor. Nor am I sure, incidentally, that I am deviating from the model that Rogers *actually* offers as I have witnessed in his own moment-to-moment relating with another person.

It will be remembered that unconditional acceptance is not the only condition for therapeutic growth that Rogers cites. Genuineness or congruence on the counsellor's part is of equal importance and it is on genuineness that I stake my right to give expression, when the moment demands it (and that moment is not always easy to identify), to those truths and values which I cherish. So great can be my own anguish when I experience the kind of self-betrayal in a client which I have described above that I feel increasingly compelled to give expression to that anguish and to the values which underpin it. As I do so I sense in myself nothing of the judgmental attitude towards the other which is the curse of moralism. Instead I experience a deep regard for my client which would make it unthinkably insulting on my part not to share as graciously and lovingly as I can those truths which give meaning to my own life and actions. My client may of course continue to reject me and reject his own apparent journey towards health but at least he will be rejecting me as a person with my feelings and values and not simply me as a counsellor wedded to a belief (often justified) in the therapeutic efficacy of moral non-intervention.

My deep desire to be genuine in my relationship with my client does not impede my acceptance of him when the ethical witness which I proclaim points to what John Hoffmann (1979), in a book bearing the same title as this chapter, has called 'an empowering acceptance at the heart of life', by which he means a source of being which validates by the very unconditionality of its acceptance all that is created. At the same time if I speak with an authority that is not truly moral I am refusing to acknowledge that for every person ethical development is a fundamental part of growth towards wholeness. This seems to me of tremendous importance. Mental health is the outcome not simply of basking in the unconditional acceptance of a person-centred therapist or being in the unreal environment of a permanent encounter group where nothing has any lasting ethical significance. Mental health is the outcome of relating what happens in therapy to the real world where moral decisions have to be made and where prejudice, injustice, oppression and degrading inequalities are rampant. Faced with such a world a person who neglects his ethical development can never hope for personal healing and a counsellor who allows that to happen in a client is ignoring an essential dimension of his therapeutic work.

The task as I see it then, is to embody as far as I am able an utterly gracious authority. I strive to adopt a response which accepts unconditionally the other person, which avoids all overtones of moralism and yet points unerringly to a non-moralistic morality whose attractiveness is irresistible. That for me is the nearest I can get (and again I am indebted to the insights of John Hoffmann) to describing a gracious authority which is truly moral. If I can embrace such an authority I shall not lapse into a posture which offers cheap grace – 'I'll forgive you whatever you do' – nor shall I run the risk of colluding with immorality by adhering to a form of therapeutic authority which forbids me to express my own deepest sense of life's meaning. I have come to conclude therefore that there will be critical times in my counselling encounters when, if I am to be fully genuine and if I am to care about the ethical growth of my client, I must seek to give expression to an authority which at one and the same time attracts my client towards the greatest effort for moral development while granting him the absolute right to be apart from such development. I do not for one moment deny the difficulty or complexity of such a task. Not only must I feel the deepest possible respect for and acceptance of my client's freedom and autonomy but I must experience also the deepest desire to be fully present in the relationship, and that includes my ethical self with all its passion and yearning. To embrace all these feelings and values within a unified response to another person is demanding enough but to give expression to them without lapsing into moralism on the one hand or empty permissiveness on the other is perhaps the stiffest challenge that any counsellor can face.

What is more I become increasingly persuaded that it is precisely this capacity in the counsellor which needs to be demonstrated at those vital times when metaphorically death threatens to take away the life of the psychologically newborn person. I have heard it said by wise midwives that it is not the moment of birth itself which demands the greatest skill and attentiveness, despite its enormous excitement, but what happens during the first hour of life. I suspect that in the case of some clients the counsellor, like the midwife, needs to be particularly alert to the fears which follow immediately upon the client's profound experience of unconditional acceptance and self-love. If these fears are such that the client moves rapidly away from life and heads back towards neurosis and destruction, then I submit it is not enough for the counsellor to remain passively acceptant of this flight from health. His response must convey that being alive and healthy is right and desirable *and* that his client who is fleeing in fear from life and health is totally acceptable. Not one or the other but both at the same time.

I have chosen to focus on the client who by his words and behaviour denies the validity of the therapeutic process and runs in angry terror from his incipient feelings of self-regard. I have done so because such behaviour causes me the deepest kind of personal anguish and constitutes the most savage assault on my own value system and ethical convictions. For others it may be a quite different form of client behaviour or expression which brings about a similar shaking of the foundations. It may be, for example, that a client is expressing every intention of committing a deed which morally the counsellor finds utterly repugnant. For the person-centred counsellor however the dilemma is the same in every case. How can he simultaneously convey his continuing acceptance and confront his client with the moral issue which lies at the heart of his struggle? I have suggested that there is much in the person-centred tradition (and in the analytical for that matter) which implies that unconditional acceptance and moral confrontation are incompatible activities. That is a view to which I can no longer subscribe. On the contrary I have come to believe that it is the very holding of these two in healthy tension which constitutes the counsellor's greatest challenge and can prove to be his most potent force for healing at those crucial times when the client hovers between health and neurosis. Such a conviction brings with it the somewhat daunting reflection that I shall have no chance whatever of offering to my client such a life-giving force unless I have succeeded in extending to myself the same healing attitude of love and challenging confrontation. To quote John Hoffmann once more, I need to experience again and again that 'empowering acceptance at the heart of life' if I am to acknowledge my yearning for a perfection which is beyond all moralism and if I am then to strive towards it however feebly and intermittently.

## References

Freud, S. (1949), *The Ego and the Id* (London, Hogarth), p. 72.

Hoffmann, John (1979), *Ethical Confrontation in Counselling* (University of Chicago Press) p. 107.

Rogers, C. R. (1965), *Client-Centered Therapy* (Boston, Houghton Mifflin), p. 48.

Thorne, Brian (1979) 'In search of value and meaning', *Theology*, 82 (January), pp. 16–24.

# 9 Choice in childbirth[1]

*Jean Towler and Gavin Fairbairn*

Over the past two decades concern about the quality of maternity care provided in Britain has resulted in increasing public support for pressure groups such as the Association for Improvements in the Maternity Services and the Active Birth Movement. Much of this concern has focused on the question whether women should be afforded choice in relation to the care they receive during pregnancy and about where and how they give birth. Although the denial of choice may be justifiable in certain circumstances, it seems that too often the obstetric will is routinely and even unthinkingly imposed so that women are often denied choice in circumstances where choice is appropriate.

In the following we examine arguments for and against giving women the opportunity to choose the place and style of their birth experience. We argue that if women are to be treated with respect as persons as well as with care as patients they must be allowed and enabled to make responsible choices throughout the course of their maternity care and treatment.

Let us begin by looking at a petition presented to Joan Lestor in 1982, which prompted her to raise issues in the House of Commons about choice in maternity care. The petition expresses concern about maternity care in Britain and calls for patients' rights to be defined in law:

> The humble petition of the Association for Improvements in the Maternity Services, the Birth Centre and the International Women's Council on Obstetrical Practice and others, herewith requests:
>
> That our parental rights be strengthened so that:
>
> 1 We choose where and how we give birth to our children.
> 2 We receive full information about any drugs, tests and interventions during our pregnancies and births.
> 3 We can withdraw our consent to routine technological intervention if we so decide.

We believe that these are inalienable human rights which are regularly denied in many British hospitals.[2]

Some, perhaps many, obstetricians will protest that it is already their practice to give women as much choice as is possible. They may assert that they already give women all the information they need and that, as in all medical practice, the patient has the right to withdraw consent at any reasonable time. For such obstetricians this petition is clearly redundant. However that it should have been drawn up and presented at all indicates a strong and continuing concern that choices in childbirth are too often made by doctors rather than by the women in question.

It is as well to make clear at the outset that although we will be arguing in favour of giving women choice as far as is possible, we do not believe that choice is always appropriate. Indeed there are circumstances in which we believe that to offer free choice would constitute negligence. However even in such circumstances women should be given as much choice as is consistent with their welfare and with the welfare of their babies. When choice is denied to a woman on the basis of sound clinical evidence, her welfare demands that she be given good reason for this. The denial of choice is discussed further later in the chapter.

## Responsibility, choice and respect for persons

That individual human beings should be treated with respect as persons is commonly regarded as one of the central values of the caring professions.[3]

John Harris[4] has suggested that respect for persons has two essential dimensions:

1  Concern for their welfare.
2  Respect for their wishes.

He writes: 'They are essential just in the sense that no one could coherently claim to respect others if their behaviour failed to exhibit both dimensions', but argues that respect for the wishes of others is the more important of these two elements. Alastair Campbell[5] comes to a similar conclusion about the importance of attending to the wishes of others if we are to treat them with respect:

> Respect... implies a relationship of involvement with other persons such that our choices and intentions are governed by their aims and aspirations as well as our own. To acknowledge another person is to acknowledge the possibility of other centres of choice and intention by which our personal aspirations may be modified. It sets in the centre of morality the language of 'we' rather than the language of 'I' and 'they'.

Both Harris and Campbell in their accounts of the attitude (and by implication behaviour) required if we are to respect others as persons, begin to attend to the importance of reciprocity in respectful personal relationships. The Christian teaching to love one's neighbour as oneself contains the essence of what we intend to draw attention to – the importance when we relate to another of recognising and relating to the other as a person rather than as an object. The 'golden rule' of Christianity, that we should do to others only what we would like them to do to us, also suggests a way of relating which seems to embody 'respect for persons'.

Taking the 'golden rule' as the basis for our notion of 'respect for persons' it follows that a doctor who intends to act in ways that are respectful of his patients as people should treat them in the way that he would like to be treated were he a patient. In relation to pregnancy and childbirth this means that a doctor should treat pregnant women as he would wish to be treated, were he pregnant. Doctors and midwives take responsibility in all their professional actions and we might assume that a doctor who becomes a patient would wish to be responsible in taking decisions about the course of his treatment; if pregnant we might assume that he would wish to take responsible decisions about, for example, the place and style of the birth of his child and about whether or not he should undergo any of the 'routine' diagnostic tests which may be conducted antenatally. In other words obstetricians and midwives who intend to treat pregnant mothers with respect as persons should give them the opportunity to make responsible choices.

Responsibility involves choice because a person cannot be responsible for what happens to her unless she has chosen to act in one way or another, or has chosen to refrain from acting. For example, she cannot be said to be responsible for having before her a plate of tripe and onions which fills her with revulsion unless it is the case either that she asked the waiter to bring it to her rather than some other more tasty morsel, or alternatively that she chose to invite some other person to choose for her. In either case the plateful before her is the result of her choice and she is responsible for its being there.

We have suggested that in order to treat them with respect as persons, doctors must permit their patients to take responsibility for themselves by making responsible choices about what happens to them. But what is involved in making responsible choices? There seem to be two important elements here; the first relates to state of information or knowledge, the second to rationality.

First, if a pregnant woman is to accept responsibility for her body and for decisions regarding medical procedures to be carried out on it, her choices must be informed choices because she cannot be responsible in choosing between two courses of action unless she knows what it is that she is choosing between. It is not good enough that she should simply choose between alternatives; she must make her choice knowing what the alternatives are between which she is choosing. The information she has must be appropriate and it must be sufficiently detailed to make the choice a real one between real alternatives. The information given must be realistic and should indicate the probabilities of things going right or wrong as well as of expected benefits and of possible side-effects.

In the case of a woman who does not fall into the low-risk category, less choice will of course be available but even in such cases some choice will be appropriate. For example, a woman who has had a previous Caesarian section may be offered the choice between an elective section and a 'trial of scar'; in such a case information would, for example, have to be given about the possibility that trying for a vaginal delivery might end in operative delivery. A mother given this information might decide that attempting to achieve a vaginal delivery is worthwhile despite the limitations that would be necessary including abstaining from oral fluids.

We are not suggesting that in order to be in a position to make informed choices, a pregnant woman must be in possession of 'all the facts' or have complete knowledge; clearly a lay person cannot understand the complexities of situations arising in relation to obstetric matters in the same way that a qualified person can. Equally clearly of course the variability of individual circumstances means that even trained doctors and midwives can never make a fully informed choice on behalf of their patients. All we are suggesting is that individual patients should be given such information as they require in order that, as far as possible, they choose in a way that accords with how they would have chosen at their most rational and most self-aware. Such information must be given in an appropriate way and at an appropriate time. For example, it should not be given when she is half asleep or unduly emotional and except in exceptional circumstances it should not be given just before the decision in question has to be taken, when other factors may be influential. Given that efforts are made in order appropriately to prepare patients for choices that may arise, there should be very few cases where pregnant women are invited to make choices when, for one reason or another, they are less capable of making rational and properly considered choices than they would be normally. Discussing possible events in advance and laying contingency plans is perhaps the best way of avoiding the possibility of an unprepared woman having to make decisions, or the possibility of someone else having to make decisions on her behalf on the grounds that she is 'in no condition' to decide for herself.

Secondly the individual must be capable of rational choice. She must be conscious, mentally stable and not suffering from mental stress such that her judgment is likely to be impaired. She must be capable of understanding explanations of her condition and of alternative treatments and their relative benefits and disadvantages. This implies both that she should be sufficiently intelligent to understand and that her grasp of English should be sufficiently good to allow understanding Where a patient's first language is not English she may have to be helped to overcome language difficulties.

Women who are not trained in midwifery or obstetrics are unlikely to have the specialist knowledge necessary to decide on courses of action while they are pregnant, especially when their pregnancies are complicated in some way. However, given access to information and the encouragement and support of professional experts, they are likely to be capable of making at least some decisions. In obstetric care doctors and midwives are responsible for ensuring that each mother is given information of a kind that is appropriate to her cultural, educational social, medical and obstetric background. They are responsible for estimating her capacity to understand explanations of procedures, and for gearing their explanations accordingly. In some circumstances this task will be easier than in others. For example, a highly educated and emotionally stable woman will be more likely to understand explanations than one who is less well educated or less emotionally secure. No matter how difficult, however, there is a responsibility to make a serious attempt to judge a mother's ability and to gauge explanations accordingly. It does not seem good enough, for example, that excuses should be made for not giving a mother information of a sufficiently detailed kind to enable real informed choice simply because of the added difficulties that this might cause. In addition doctors and midwives should not try to persuade a woman by pressure of authority superior knowledge or moral arguments to choose in any one direction rather than another.

It might be claimed that in relation to medical care 'most' people would prefer that choices are made by their medical practitioner. A person may choose to allow someone else to choose for her; it was in this way that the unfortunate individual mentioned earlier came to be faced with a plate of tripe and onions. Inevitably some pregnant women will choose to hand over responsibility to the doctor as patients often do in other areas of medicine. However the giving up of future choices in itself constitutes choice. In any case it is not suggested that women must be forced to choose if they are to be treated respectfully, rather that they should be given the opportunity to choose. It is worth considering that a mother who apparently chooses that a doctor should choose and make decisions for her may not have made a genuine choice. It may be that the opportunity to gain sufficiently good information in order that she can make genuine choices and decisions of her own has been denied. It may be that she was unaware of her opportunity to choose or that she had the right to do so or alternatively that she came under moral and professional pressure to make one choice rather than another. She may, for example, have been told that she could choose but that if as a result something went wrong, she would only have herself to blame.

## Choices during pregnancy and childbirth

Throughout pregnancy and childbirth numerous choices have to be made. These relate, for example, to the style of antenatal and maternity care that is given and received, to tests that may be undertaken, to the place and style of birth and so on. Some of these will now be examined.

*Where* the mother is booked for birth is highly significant in that the choice of intended place of birth effectively determines the type of antenatal care and the style of delivery; that is, the technological/ pharmacological style which is the norm in consultant units or the natural/physiological style typical of birth in the home or GP/midwife unit. If she is unaware that choice is possible a 'low risk' mother may automatically be booked for consultant care and thereafter be referred to as his patient (which implies illness). In consequence she is more likely to regard herself as such than a woman whose attendants use some other term, for example 'mother'. The way in which a pregnancy is viewed, for example as a natural biological event or as a potential pathological condition, is determined by the approach adopted by the pregnant woman's attendants. Those women whose pregnancies are pathological or complicated by concurrent physical illness are appropriately termed, and treated as, patients. However, as most pregnancies are neither pathological nor complicated by disease, most pregnant women are not appropriately termed, nor treated as, 'patients'.

Healthy low-risk mothers who choose GP/midwife booking or home birth, will receive the majority of their antenatal care from the GP and midwife and will remain under their care until or unless there is deviation from the normal. These are less likely to be treated as patients, and rightly so.

### Testing

After the choice of style of care has been made most other choices during pregnancy relate to procedures which may be carried out on the mother in order to assess the baby's health. What may appear to be simply a matter of routine to the practitioners involved, actually involves choice; for example between carrying out a procedure or omitting it, or between one procedure and another. For example, the choice whether or not to carry out the rubella antibody test in order to discover whether a mother is already immune to German measles is often regarded as routine, as is the alpha-feto protein test which is believed by many to give a good indication of the possibility or otherwise that a baby is handicapped. Amniocentesis is often regarded as a routine follow-up for mothers whose alpha-feto protein levels are beyond the upper limits of normal, as well as for mothers whose age puts them in a 'high risk' group in relation to the possibility of having conceived a child with certain disorders, notably Down's syndrome; one reason for amniocentesis is to allow mothers the option of aborting such a child. Finally the use of ultrasonic scans to screen for foetal abnormalities in instances where other evidence suggests possible problems is regarded as routine by many.

Diagnostic tests have become a routine part of antenatal care and management. Although choices are made about whether or not these tests should be performed, they are often made by doctors without women consenting to them or even being informed that they are being, or have been, made. That such tests, some of which are not without risk,[6] are often performed as standard practice raises ethical questions, for example about the possibility that women are subjected without their properly informed consent to tests to which they would not consent were they informed. Clear guidelines are to be found in a variety of places, for example, in the government report, *Maternity Care in Action*:

> It is important that the reasons for procedures and tests and their results should be explained to each woman. She should be given the opportunity to decline tests. Tests for fetal abnormalities in particular must only be undertaken with the woman's informed consent.

In spite of such statements the petition cited earlier suggests that many women are still not informed that they have the right to choose whether or not to have tests during their pregnancy.

Even when policies allow that women are to be given choice, what this frequently means is that they are to be allowed to 'opt out' of routine procedures rather than that they should be given a free choice. This means that in order to exercise the right to choose, a woman has to choose against medical advice.

*The timing of birth: induction and acceleration of labour*
Labour can be induced or accelerated by the use of oxytocic drugs and so there is real choice about when babies will be born. A doctor may choose to stimulate contractions artificially in cases where a mother's health is endangered, for example in pre-eclampsia. However while there are sound reasons for induction of labour in some cases it may be,

and often is, performed in others in the absence of valid obstetric indications and against the mother's wishes. For example, it is not only in circumstances where, in the opinion of medical personnel, it will benefit the mother and baby that the time of birth may be chosen. The choice to induce or accelerate birth may be made for administrative or professional reasons; for example because it is convenient to have babies born during the day when the full range of laboratory and other 'back-up' services are available. This raises issues of resource allocation which will not be considered here. We wish simply to suggest that mothers should not be induced without their informed agreement. If the choice to induce is to be made in order to ensure that maximum technological expertise is available, then it is one in which the woman concerned should be at least an equal partner. Where there is good reason to believe that either mother or baby will need special help, there will be good reason for offering arguments to a mother about speeding up her labour while daytime resources are available. However even in such circumstances, if women are to be treated with respect as persons, the arguments offered should not be coercive or paternalistic and women should be allowed to choose whether or not the procedures in question should be carried out. This should be the case except in those rare instances where a mother's choice is thought to be so potentially dangerous for her baby or for herself that a doctor is prepared to override her wishes for its sake or for her sake. When induction is the result of a medical decision the woman will be denied the possibility of choosing to await the onset of spontaneous physiological labour at the time her body dictates, or would dictate if given the chance.

Another choice that is available in relation to the timing of birth is the length of time that the second or 'birthing' stage of labour is allowed to continue. Over the years this stage has had time limits imposed on it and has been gradually contracted to one hour and in many cases to half an hour. When time limits are imposed by an arbitrary policy, a doctor or midwife adhering to such a policy is more likely to perform an episiotomy to expedite delivery than in circumstances where there is no arbitrarily imposed constraint on the length of time the second stage may last.

In some cases a midwife or doctor may have defensible reasons for choosing to cut an episiotomy, for example because of foetal distress. On the other hand they may choose to undertake this procedure for indefensible reasons. For example they may feel they have waited long enough, or it may almost be time to go off duty. John Finch writes that 'a routine episiotomy (unnecessary and objected to) is indefensible and a serious assault and battery against the patient'.[8] Episiotomy has become an obstetric fashion and is regularly performed as a prophylactic measure to prevent muscle tearing. Even a midwife or doctor who is largely in favour of giving mothers a choice may be unwilling to take the risk of such damage, if, for example, she had had the experience of having a mother suffer third-degree tearing while in her care. As a result she may begin to cut episiotomies in circumstances where formerly she would not have done so.[9] Such self-defensive measures result from taking one's accountability for the care of another person to involve not only having to account for, that is, explain and justify, what one has done or has not done in relation to them but also the acceptance of blame when things go wrong, even in circumstances where the ascription of blame is inappropriate because one has made one's decisions responsibly and has not been negligent.[10] In such circumstances it is understandable that a midwife or doctor may wish to guard her reputation against possible accusations of carelessness. However it is important to note that guarding one's reputation is not a good enough reason for cutting a labouring mother. After all the chances are that the perineal muscle will not suffer serious tearing and may not even tear at all. We wish to emphasise that a professional's decision that a prophylactic incision would be appropriate removes from a mother the choice of risking a tear rather than certainly having a stitched incision, unless she is given the choice whether or not it should be performed. And it goes without saying that statements of the kind, 'Now we're just going to do an episiotomy to stop you from tearing; you wouldn't want to tear, would you?' are not acceptable preambles to an incision.

### The place and style of birth

Hospital confinement has increasingly become the norm during the past twenty years mainly because of the claim that hospital births are safer than home births. This idea is based on the readiness with which technological aids are available in hospitals and the assumption that technology and safety go hand in hand. The argument given to mothers contemplating home delivery often goes something like this: 'But if anything goes wrong surely it is better to be in the right place where all the help is readily available.' (Note the moralistic overtones and lack of worthwhile information in such a statement.) But medical opinion is not unanimous in believing that hospital confinement is better or even safer:

> On the one hand there is the view of the obstetric establishment which states a clear intention to aim for 100 per cent hospital confinements; while on the other, there are individuals both within the medical profession and outside who feel that women should be allowed to have their confinements at the place of their choice (assuming no overriding contra indications) until such time as it has been shown that this is a course of action that is either inadvisable or unacceptable on medical, social or economic grounds.[11]

In practice hospital confinement, except where it takes place in a GP/midwife unit, is likely to involve the use of a surfeit of technology. Although there is widespread agreement that for a small number of cases, where babies are at high risk for one reason or another, maximum intervention is necessary, doctors on both sides of the debate agree that there is little evidence to support many of the clinical practices advocated by obstetricians. In spite of this many doctors continue to support the use of technology, sometimes in a manner that is unthinking or even worse. So for example one strong protagonist for the use of technology, who admits that there is a lack of evidence for its benefits, offers a bizarre view of the ethics of the situation. He writes that since the technology is available, 'we think it unethical not to use it'.[12] This is like advocating the nuclear holocaust on the grounds that since the technology to blow ourselves to pieces is available it would be wrong simply to argue about its deployment.

While some obstetricians remain convinced that the practice of technological birth (which of course necessitates hospital confinement) is justified by obstetric considerations, others argue that such management is not necessarily judicious, particularly for the large number of mothers who fall within the low-risk category. Such doctors, aware that invasive techniques, such as induction and augmentation of labour and continuous electronic heart monitoring by scalp electrode, have become more widely used in recent times, would recognise that the benefits in using such techniques have to be weighed against the potential hazards that they involve.[13]

Some obstetricians clearly believe that where the use of a given technique can be shown to have some benefit they are justified in using it without reference to the mother's wishes. Others however believe that even where the use of technological procedures can be justified on clinical grounds, the application of such procedures without reference to the mother concerned is wrong. For example, Huntingford writes, 'not all technological advance results in acceptable improvements and especially not if it is applied arbitrarily, without selection, without evaluation, without reference to consumers and by depriving them of choice'.[14] But it is not just because applying technology routinely and arbitrarily deprives pregnant and labouring mothers of choice that some doctors believe the fashion for technology is wrong. They also have clinical grounds. For example, discussing the dominant mode of birth in consultant obstetric units, Kerr writes, 'obstetric practices such as the intuitively absurd supine position and the administration of unwanted narcotic painkillers have no scientific or human justi-fication'.[15] The practice of expecting women to adopt the supine position for the second stage of labour is largely related to the need to keep a mother confined because of the limitations imposed by the use of technology in birth. House writes: 'The worst thing we've done is to put women back into bed on their backs into what is known as the "stranded beetle" position, which reduces the placental blood flow by compressing the large blood vessels.'[16] A consequence of this is that foetal oxygenation could be reduced.

The Peel Report of 1970 advocated 100 per cent hospital confinement on the grounds that hospital was the safest place for birth. However, although the Report's assertion that hospital is safer was based on an examination of statistics drawn from the 1958 Perinatal Mortality Survey,[18] it did not present convincing statistical evidence in support of its advocacy of hospital confinement. The 1958 Survey had shown that as the trend to hospital confinement rose, so perinatal mortality fell. The members of the Peel Committee assumed a simple cause and effect relationship which favoured hospital confinement. The obstetric establishment quickly accepted and built upon this assumption, claiming that the use of modern technology was a major contributory factor. Many obstetricians were and still are genuinely convinced that high-technology birthing leads to lower perinatal mortality rates. Others in medicine are clearly sceptical about the reasons some obstetricians might have for welcoming research which can be used to support their wish to have more babies born in hospital consultant units. For example, considering the unwillingness of the establishment to reconsider the evidence of the 1958 Survey, Luke Zander[19] writes:

> Having based their whole argument on one of safety, the reluctance of the profession to consider this evidence objectively... suggests that their decision has been made on preconceived assumptions which they are not willing to reconsider in the light of available evidence.

Zander is clearly very suspicious of the motivation behind this reluctance which he thinks might 'cast doubt in some minds as to whether the reasons for it stem principally from a concern for patient care, or principally from intraprofessional self-interest'. He points out that:

> not only is home confinement/natural birthing a form of care which is unknown to consultants but by its emphasis on non-interference and with its absence of technical monitoring facilities it might be said to challenge and even threaten the principles on which his own form of management is based.

He argues that 'Rational decisions are not always easy when one's beliefs are being challenged.' Is it appropriate, he asks, to allow decision-making about obstetric care to remain almost solely in the hands of 'those who by virtue of making obstetrics their speciality have acquired a perspective that, although highly advanced scientifically, has restricted their view of the human experience of childbirth?'

Some obstetricians may be so unwilling to abdicate power and control that they will withdraw their support from GPs who allow their patients to exercise choice as to where and how to give birth. It could be argued that a consultant who does this would be interfering with the right and responsibility of colleagues in general practice to fulfil their role as personal physicians who are familiar with the social and psychological, as well as obstetric, needs of the woman. In the same way obstetricians who make policy decisions on clinical practice interfere with the clinical judgment of the midwife and with her right to make choices as a professional practitioner of normal midwifery who must be accountable for her actions, her judgment and the care she gives to mothers and babies.

The presumption that hospital birth was safer was accepted by members of the Short Committee in 1980.[20] As a result they continued to advocate total hospital confinement. In addition they advocated maximum use of birth technology. They envisaged that as numbers of obstetricians, paediatricians and machines increased the perinatal mortality rate would drop significantly. This committee was either unaware of or chose to ignore Marjorie Tew's challenge[21, 22, 23] on statistical grounds to the belief that birth in hospital is safer. Tew[21] re-examined the statistics on the basis of which the Peel Report first advocated 100 per cent hospital confinement. She found that the correlation between the home confinement rate and the perinatal mortality rate was too low to be statistically significant. Having analysed all the available data she was surprised to find no evidence to support the claim that 100 per cent hospital births was something worth aiming at. She concluded that 'there is no causal relationship between hospital birth and lower perinatal mortality rate' and asserted that 'the move towards increased hospitalisation for birth cannot be justified on the basis of the evidence reported in the 1970 British Births Survey'.[22] In doing so she offered an alternative explanation of the statistics: 'The statistics support the hypothesis that reductions in mortality are more likely to result from improvements in the general health of the mothers and their fitness to reproduce than from innovations in scientific obstetrics, however sophisticated.'[23] Such a view is supported by Huntingford:[24]

> Most of the fall in maternal and perinatal mortality has been attributed to scientific advance and to the concentration of maternity care in the hands of specialists. However, the improvements in obstetric performance could equally well be accounted for by social changes, such as more women bearing at a safer age (ie fewer very young or old women having babies); an overall improvement in standards of living, especially among those least well off; a reduction in the number of mothers of very large families, a general increase in the standards of nutrition and stature of women; general improvement in maternal and child care because more people are better informed.

Campbell and McFarlane's recent study, *Where to be born*,[25] further supports the idea that hospital is by no means certainly the most safe place for all women to give birth; they write: 'There is no evidence to support the claim that the safest place is for all women to give birth in hospital.'

We have examined the background to the current practice of encouraging women to have babies in hospital rather than in the home, along with some of the criticisms that have been made of the arguments in favour of hospital confinement as a safer way of having babies. We want now to look more closely at some of the differences between different places and styles of delivery.

Over the last few years the style of birth has developed into a highly contentious issue. In practice the *way* in which a mother gives birth is very often determined by the *place* of birth. Frequently the decision about place of birth is made for a woman by her GP because in his opinion hospital is safer and/or better for her, or perhaps, as Zander suggests, because he has been intimidated by threat of lack of support into accepting the local obstetrician's policy.

Let us look at the alternative places of birth that are currently available and at the differences that context can make to the style of delivery and consequently to a mother's experience of childbirth. Basically the choice to be made is between a natural/physiological birth at home or in a GP/midwife unit, and a technological/pharmacological birth in a hospital consultant unit, although natural/physiological birth is becoming acceptable in some consultant obstetric units.

*Birth in a consultant obstetric Unit.* In such units women are literally *confined* within a formal and sophisticated clinical/technological environment. They are surrounded by machinery, medical gas cylinders and all the other paraphernalia of modern technological obstetrics. The lights are bright, the environment is clinical (even sterile) in appearance. Some mothers may feel reassured that should the need arise 'all the modern equipment' is near at hand and ready. On the other hand even for such a woman the atmosphere of the consultant labour suite may militate against her feeling calm and relaxed. Rather than being conducive to relaxation (which few people would deny is in turn conducive to ease of birth), such an environment can provoke anxiety and in turn increase pain perception. Research has shown that anxiety causes release of catecholamines (adrenalines) which can disturb the physiological pattern of contraction. 'Adrenaline has a direct effect on uterine muscle, decreasing uterine contractions and thereby increasing the length of labour.'[26]

Medical intervention, for example the induction or acceleration of labour by intravenous infusion of uterine stimulants, is common in deliveries which take place in consultant obstetric units, perhaps because they are readily available. In practice the introduction of such interventions often has a 'cascade effect' with more technology and medication being required in response to induced tension and distress. A mother launched on such an obstetric trajectory, in all probability linked to a machine, with a cardiotograph belt, foetal scalp electrode and maybe epidural catheter in position, has no choice but to give birth in bed. The chances are that her delivery will also be aided by an episiotomy, the separation of the placenta and membranes hastened by the use of another oxytocic drug and their delivery hastened by controlled cord traction. These latter techniques are unlikely to be discussed with the mother so she is unlikely to be offered any real choice as to whether they are or are not performed.

A mother may choose to deliver in an obstetric unit because she feels safe with technology, knows she can have total pain relief, or feels happy in the knowledge that expert help is on hand if any complications arise. Every woman should be entitled so to choose but should be equally entitled to choose an alternative place and mode of labour and birth.

*Birth at home.* A mother may choose to give birth at home where she can feel safer and more in control of what is happening to her. She may choose thus because she wishes to register her disapproval of arbitrary obstetric policies applied indiscriminately. Such a mother has typically been motivated to find out about the possible ways in which her baby can be born. She values the freedom to make choices and may have the idea that if she gives birth at home she is more likely to be treated as an individual than as a statistic. Her investigations into the ways in which she may give birth and the relative benefits and hazards of these has typically led her to rebel against mechanised birth and to want to participate fully in a natural birth in the belief that such a birth may confer physiological and psychological advantages on her baby. Too often such mothers are seen as rather defiant and uncooperative. Mothers who, for similar reasons, wish to give birth in a GP/midwife unit are likely to be similarly labelled.

In reality a woman's reasons for opting for home birth may be that she has learned that her local obstetric unit offers little choice. And so in order that she can birth in a place where she has the opportunity to make responsible choices about the management of her labour and the birth of her baby, and where she can avoid a full blown 'high-tech' birth, she may feel forced to choose home birth. This will be the case unless she is fortunate enough to live in an area with a GP/midwife unit which embraces the new gentle approach to birth. She may choose home birth even though she would have preferred to have had her non-technological or natural labour in hospital with technological help readily available should it prove necessary, because in reality there are few such GP/midwife units. Failing to provide a relaxed non-clinical atmosphere within obstetric units or adjacent GP/midwife units can thus paradoxically lead women to opt for a 'low-tech at any cost' birth at home rather than a 'no tech if possible' birth in a place where they can opt for the use of technology should the need arise.

Labour and childbirth at home are conducive to a relaxed and positive birth experience for both mother and baby. The private and familiar environment is likely to help reduce tension. The labouring woman can have lights as low or as bright as she wishes, she can move about freely, bath and use the toilet as she wishes. A mother who labours and gives birth at home will not have an enema or be shaved unless she requests this; she is much less likely to have an episiotomy than if she was giving birth in hospital. She is free to adopt whatever posture she wishes throughout labour; she can respond to her own sense of what will be best for her baby rather than having to perform as expected. The emotional climate at home combined with the lack of tension caused by bright lights, strange surroundings, machinery, lack of freedom to move and act as she wishes, is likely to help a mother to relax. This in turn is likely to enhance the physiological processes of labour,[27] as well as having psychological advantages for both mother and baby.

As we have said, one of the mainstays of the argument for hospital confinement is that it is safer, an assertion for which there is little evidence. On the other hand there is some evidence to suggest that confinement at home is at least as safe and perhaps even safer. If this is the case then another reason for choosing home confinement is that it may be safer than hospital confinement. This is exactly what Tew claims. She writes, 'Birth in an obstetric hospital is much less safe, not only for normal births, but also for many births with some kind of abnormality.'[28] And a study of 5000 home births in Holland, where the perinatal mortality rate is enviably low, showed that none of the few deaths that occurred at home could have been avoided if the birth had taken place in hospital.[29]

It is important to note that in any examination of statistical evidence about the relative safety of home and hospital births, the reasons that birth took place in either place are very important. An analysis of 8856 births in England and Wales in 1979[30] revealed that where the birth was planned for home and all the 'back-up' arrangements had been made, home birth was actually as safe as, or safer than, birth in hospital. Where home was the intended place of delivery the perinatal mortality rate was 4.1 per thousand: this figure does not take into account the women who booked for home births but were transferred to hospital during labour. When such transfers are accounted for estimates suggest that the overall perinatal mortality rate for home births could be as much as doubled. Even so the rate is still below the overall national perinatal mortality rate. The objective of this new analysis was to exclude unplanned home births such as babies born to teenagers whose pregnancies were concealed, and premature or precipitate births in women booked for hospital delivery: the mortality rate in both these groups is inevitably high.

*GP/midwife unit delivery*. In reality obstetric units and home are two extremes but the arguments applied against home as a place of birth, that is, because of its lack of medical expertise and technological aids, cannot be sustained if a mother chooses to have her baby in a GP/midwife unit in a hospital. Such a unit within a hospital, which as far as possible simulates home and where the mother has freedom of choice as for a home confinement, but where medical and technical facilities are held in reserve, provides the 'best of both worlds'. Indeed GP units were deemed to be a 'safe and sensible compromise' by a Joint Committee of the Royal College of Obstetricians and Gynaecologists and the Royal College of General Practitioners.[31] However these units are not universally available and in any case the GP may not support the choice of such a unit; he may wish to avoid the possibility of being called out during the night or may feel unable to undertake perineal suturing should this be required of him. For such reasons low-risk mothers may lose out on the possibility of a GP/midwife unit delivery. Alternatively a consultant may impose a set of criteria for admission to such a unit which severely limits the mother's choice. Such criteria might, for example, exclude all primagravidae as well as women over thirty or those who have had a miscarriage. In other words, in order to be considered suitable for delivery outside a consultant unit many obstetricians require a mother to have not only an unblemished obstetric and medical history but also a proven 'track record' of unproblematic birth.

**Concluding remarks**
We began by suggesting that in order to treat them with respect as persons, those charged with the care of parturient women should involve them in responsible decision-making throughout their pregnancies and at the time of birth. If, as we have argued, it is not possible to choose responsibly without having adequate information, pregnant women will have to be prepared for choice in a way that takes into account their individual needs and background. They will have to be given the information they need, in an appropriate way and at an appropriate time. For example, if a woman is to choose the intended and expected place of her delivery she will have to be told about the options

available when she first seeks medical advice about her pregnancy. She will have to be given information about the relative advantages and disadvantages of home delivery, delivery in a GP/midwife unit and in a consultant obstetric unit. Preparation classes for childbirth will have to include teaching on more natural styles of birthing as well as about conventional confinement. In addition, if a woman is genuinely to be allowed to choose where and how her baby is born, she will have to be allowed to make realistic changes to the choice she makes initially in the light of information she gains from such classes and in the light of any complications arising during the course of her pregnancy.

We discussed some of the opportunities for choice during pregnancy up to and including the time of birth. In relation to routine testing we drew attention to the guidelines contained within the government publication, *Maternity Care in Action*, which state that women should be given valid information about tests and the opportunity to decline such tests. In order that women should be given a free choice in such matters they should be allowed to opt for testing rather than having to opt out of what is an established procedure. We also discussed some of the differences between birth in different contexts, paying particular attention to their advantages and disadvantages. We discussed some of the arguments used by those whose aim is to achieve a situation in which all births take place in hospital and went on to consider some of the reasons why this is neither necessary nor judicious, particularly for mothers in the low-risk category. There seems, we suggested, to be little evidence to support the view that confinement in a consultant obstetric unit is superior to birth in a GP/midwife unit or at home and some to suggest that the latter might be preferable, particularly in the light of the very forceful statistical arguments of Marjorie Tew.

Since there seem to be no sound grounds for structuring maternity services so that all (or even most) deliveries take place in the highly technical/clinical atmosphere of hospital obstetric units, we can see no reason why, in the absence of legitimate financial constraints, healthy, 'low risk' women should not be given a free choice about where and how they have their babies. Since there is some evidence to suggest that the alternatives to consultant obstetric units as places for birthing are at least as safe if not safer than consultant units, it seems that such alternatives should be provided. For example, as an alternative to clinically-oriented consultant obstetric units there seem to be good grounds for making more freely available the opportunity for women to give birth in the less clinical environment of GP/midwife units which can offer more choice while having the security of emergency facilities near at hand. In addition, in the absence of evidence to suggest that more natural styles of delivery are harmful, there seems to be no reason why more possibilities for choice should not be made available by providing alternatives to current clinical and technological procedures of birth within consultant units as the rule, rather than, as at present, the exception. Indeed if a large number of women are not to be forced into a position where to have the possibility of choice in mode of birth they have to opt for home delivery without emergency operative facilities readily available, maximum choice should be offered *within* obstetric units.

So we have argued in favour of increasing the opportunities for choice extended to pregnant women in relation to the care they receive throughout pregnancy and at the time of delivery. One argument against giving women choice is that in the end the doctor or midwife is professionally accountable for what happens to the women in their care. Of course we do not suggest that women should be allowed to make choices unless they are willing to take responsibility for them, as fundamental to the idea that women should be allowed to choose is their willingness to take responsibility for such choices. If patients in general were allowed to take informed choices, thus becoming responsible for decisions rather than simply giving a watered down kind of consent to procedures decided upon by doctors, there would be fewer problems in allowing choice to patients in medicine as a whole and to pregnant women within obstetrics and midwifery in particular.

But what of the doctor? Is he to have any choice about the way in which he conducts his professional practice? Must he do what his patients and pregnant women ask, or even demand, of him? Of course we are not suggesting this. Doctors have rights just as pregnant women have. In addition to circumstances in which he has sound clinical reasons for restricting choice, a doctor may be justified in refusing to continue to attend a woman who will not accept his advice. He may not accept that there *are* alternative methods and places for giving birth and therefore may not concede that there are choices to be made. The possibility that a doctor's refusal to be involved in alternative methods may result from stubbornness to consider evidence in its favour was suggested by Zander in the article referred to earlier. It could be argued that the consultant has an ethical duty to keep himself informed of alternative birthing methods and about their validity not only in terms of physiological, obstetric and safety considerations but also in terms of the extent to which they meet the psychological, emotional and spiritual needs and beliefs of the mother. Where he does not wish to be involved in meeting a woman's expressed wishes about style of antenatal care and delivery, for whatever reasons, a doctor has a responsibility to inform her that he no longer wishes to be her attendant, that she has the right to seek alternative assistance, and where possible, to refer her to a colleague who is more sympathetic to her point of view.

It may be argued that if free choice about style of birth were available some mothers, exercising the right to choose a non-technological birth, might make very unsuitable choices and deprive their unborn children of the right to a safe delivery and the maximum chance of being healthy. Here there is a conflict of interests between mother and baby. Withholding or at any rate limiting choice may be justified on the grounds that the interests of the child are at stake and that it, like its mother, is the doctor's responsibility. In addition he may be justified in not allowing a particular choice on the basis that it is potentially so dangerous that it could result in the use of scarce and expensive resources.

Since pregnancy is a natural physiological condition in the majority of women, the majority of women should be offered as much choice about their maternity care as is compatible with the availability of resources. While we have argued that it is highly desirable and ethically right for women in the 'low risk' group to choose, it is not always appropriate for mothers at risk to be offered a free choice of *place* of birth. This is because these women may have medical or obstetric conditions which legitimate their treatment as patients of an obstetrician and/or a physician, for example a mother who is diabetic or has an obstetric complication of pregnancy.

The way in which maternity services operate in this country means that most women have no choice other than to be regarded as the 'patients' of obstetricians. Irrespective of the absence or presence of risk factors most pregnant women are routinely referred to a hospital consultant clinic and thereafter receive care which is based on a paternalistic and pathological approach to pregnancy in which they are largely denied opportunities for responsible choice. The reasons for this organisation, which results in the systematic denial of choice to many women, seem to stem principally from a lack of acknowledgement on the part of the British obstetric establishment that the majority of women are healthy and have uncomplicated pregnancies and hence do not require specialist medical care and supervision throughout pregnancy and birth. If maternity care in Britain was reorganised in a way that took account of pregnancy as a natural phenomenon most pregnant women could choose to be cared for by their GP and/or midwife, who as independent practitioners are licensed to provide antenatal, intrapartum and post-partum care in normal pregnancy. They could thus choose to receive maternity care in a context within which approaches to pregnancy as a natural phenomenon requiring the minimum of medical intervention was both likely and appropriate. This would no doubt be a good thing for those women and their babies. It would also free the facilities of highly equipped consultant obstetric units for those mothers with medical and/or obstetric problems that warrant their use and the specialist medical care that consultant obstetricians can provide.

# Notes

1 Throughout we refer to choices in pregnancy and childbirth as if they concern women exclusively; the reason for this is that it is women's bodies that become pregnant and receive care from obstetricians and midwives. Of course we recognise that men will often be involved in making decisions about the way in which their partners are cared for during pregnancy and at the time of birth. To avoid clumsiness of style we have at times referred only to 'obstetricians' when it would be more correct to refer to 'obstetricians and midwives' or 'doctors and midwives'.

2 Association for Improvement in Maternity Services (1983), *Denial of Parents' Rights in Maternity Care*, February.

3 Downie, R. S. and Telfer, E. (1969), *Respect for Persons*. London, Allen and Unwin.

4 Harris, J. (1985), *The Value of Life*. London, RKP.

5 Campbell, A. V. (1975), *Moral Problems in Medicine*. Edinburgh, Churchill Livingstone.

6 See, for example, Turnbull, A. L. and Fairweather, D. *et. al.* (1978), 'An assessment of the hazards of amniocentesis', *British Journal of Obstetrics and Gynaecology*, 85, Suppl. 2.

7 Maternity Services Advisory Committee (1982), *Maternity Care in Action*, Pt. 1, *Antenatal Care*. London, HMSO.

8 Finch, J. (1982), 'Legal route to life', Nursing Mirror, 27 October.

9 This would be an example of what Thomas Scheff implies is 'overtreatment in medicine'. Scheff, T. J. (1965), 'Decision rules, types of error and their consequences in medical diagnosis' in Massarik, F. and Ratoosh, eds (1965), *Mathematical Explorations in Behavioural Science*. Homewood, Ill., R. D. Irwin, Dorsey Press.

10 The moral dangers of adopting a negative view of accountability are discussed by Fairbairn, G. J. (1985), 'Responsibility in social work' in Watson, D. (1985), *A Code of Ethics for Social Work: the second step*. London, RKP.

11 Zander, L. (1981), 'The place of confinement: a question of statistics or ethics', *Journal of Medical Ethics*, 7, pp. 125-7.

12 Elstein, M. (1982), 'Childbirth: whose right to decide?', *Sunday Times*, 7 March.

13 *Report of the RCOG Working Party on Antenatal and Intrapartum Care* (1982). Royal College of Obstetricians and Gynaecologists, September.

14 Huntingford, P. (1978), 'Obstetric practice: past, present and future' in Kitzinger, S. and Davis, J. A., eds, *Place of Birth*. Oxford University Press.

15 Kerr, M. (1982), *Guardian*, 12 August.

16 House, M. (1982), 'Childbirth: whose right to decide?', *Sunday Times*, 7 March.

17 *Report of the Sub-Committee of the Standing Maternity and Midwifery Advisory Committee on Domiciliary Midwifery and Maternity Bed Needs* (Peel Report) (1970). DHSS, Welsh Office, Central Health Services Council, London, HMSO.

18 Butler, N. R. and Bonham, D. G. (1963), *Perinatal Mortality*. Edinburgh, E. and S. Livingstone.

19 Zander, L. (1981), 'The place of confinement: a question of statistics or ethics', *Journal of Medical Ethics*, 7, pp. 125-7.

20 Social Services Committee (Short Committee) (1980), *Report*. DHSS.

21 Tew, M. (1977), 'Where to be born', *New Society*, 20 January.

22 Tew, M. (1978), 'Intended place of delivery and perinatal outcomes', *Journal of the Royal College of General Practitioners*, 25 March, pp. 1139-46.

23 Tew, M. (1982), 'Obstetrics versus midwifery: the verdict of the statistics', *Journal of Maternal and Child Health*, May.

24 Huntingford, P. (1978), 'Obstetric practice: past, present and future' in Kitzinger, S. and Davis, J. A., eds, *Place of Birth*. Oxford University Press.

25 R. Campbell and A. MacFarlane (1987), *Where to be Born*. Oxford, National Epidemiology Unit.

26 Zuspan, F. P. (1962), 'Myometrial and cardiovascular responses to alterations in plasma epinephrine and norepinephrine', *American Journal of Obstetrics and*

*Gynaecology*, 84.
27   Holt, J., MacLennan, A. H. and Carrie, L. E. S. (1977), 'Lumbar puncture analgesi
     in labour: relation to fetal malposition and instrumental delivery', *British Medica
     Journal*, 1.
28   Tew, M. (1981), Letter to the *Guardian*, 20 June.
29   Kloosterman, G. L. (1975), cited in Suzanne Arms, *Immaculate Deception*. Boston
     Houghton Mifflin.
30   R. Campbell *et al.* (1984), 'Home births in England and Wales, 1979: perinata
     mortality according to intended place of delivery', *British Medical Journal*, 289, 2
     September.
31   RCOG and RCGP (1981), *Joint Working Party Report on Training for Obstetrics an
     Gynaecology for General Practitioners*.

# 10 Towards an institution of surrogacy

*Edgar Page*

Surrogate motherhood has aroused considerable popular interest and by and large a good deal of hostility. This is reflected in the Warnock Report on Human Fertilisation and Embryology[1] which includes recommendations for legislation aimed at suppressing all forms of surrogacy. In this paper I shall put forward a theory which could provide a basis for acceptable institutionalised surrogacy.[2] I do not discuss commercial surrogacy.

The most familiar form of surrogacy is where a woman agrees to have a child by normal pregnancy for an infertile married couple, the commissioning parents. Quite often the surrogate mother is impregnated with sperm from the husband of the commissioning parents, usually by artificial insemination but sometimes by sexual intercourse. Clearly the surrogate is the genetic mother of the resulting child. Therefore I shall call her a 'genetic' surrogate.

Genetic surrogacy is fraught with difficulties so before trying to say anything about it I shall turn to a less familiar but also less fraught type of surrogacy, which I call 'gestatory'. A gestatory surrogate supplies only the functions of gestation and birth for the commissioning parents. The embryo, probably produced from the gametes (sperm and egg) of the commissioning parents, is fertilised *in vitro* and then transferred to the uterus of the gestatory surrogate where it is hoped it will implant and develop in the normal way. As the gestatory surrogate does not supply the egg there is no genetic link between her and the resulting child.

Many people find this type of surrogacy less problematic morally than genetic surrogacy. Consider the following example. A childless couple want a child. They can produce their own viable gametes but the woman is unable to have a pregnancy for medical reasons. There is no question of adoption and in any case they are strongly motivated to have a child from their own gametes if they possibly can. By normal standards they are likely to be competent and loving parents. Clearly there is a strong case for saying that if a child could be brought into existence for them from their own gametes it should be done. Unfortunately artificial wombs have not yet been developed. However with modern techniques it is possible for another woman to gestate their embryo for them. If someone, possibly a friend or relative, wants to help them in this way as a gestatory surrogate it is difficult to see why she should not be allowed to do so.

Let us suppose then the embryo of the (commissioning) couple is transferred to the uterus of a gestatory surrogate and that on both sides there is a clear understanding that when the child is born it will be returned to the commissioning parents for them to rear as their own child. We need to ask whether in this case the commissioning parents are the child's true parents. It seems plain to me that they are, but not everyone would agree. For example, the Warnock Committee adopts the rule that the woman who gives birth to the child should always be considered to be its mother, even in this case. Yet in this kind of case, that is, in gestatory surrogacy, it is difficult to see the justice in denying the claim of the commissioning parents to the child.

The problem arises partly because in gestatory surrogacy the woman who gives birth to the child is not its genetic mother. Before the development of embryo transfer there was never any question but that the woman who gave birth to the child was its mother. Now embryo transfer can result in situations where the woman who bears the child and the genetic mother are different people and we have to choose between them in deciding who is the true mother of the child.

In the above example of gestatory surrogacy the genetic mother, not the woman who bears the child, seems to be the true mother. However we cannot say that the genetic mother is always the true mother. For example, if an infertile woman wanting a child of her own agrees to be implanted with a donated embryo (or with an embryo from a donated egg fertilised *in vitro* with her husband's sperm), surely she must be considered to be the mother of the resulting child even though she is not its genetic mother. In this case the Warnock rule seems to give the correct answer. But it is vitally important that here the embryo, or the egg, is donated. The woman acquires parental rights and duties in respect of the child as the recipient of the donated egg or embryo, not just because she gives birth to the child.

In gestatory surrogacy the embryo is transferred to the uterus of the surrogate but is not donated to her. Indeed it is the clear intention of the commissioning parents that the embryo should still belong to them and that the child should be theirs. The gestatory surrogate explicitly agrees to this. This is the important difference between a gestatory surrogate and a woman who receives a donated embryo.

The donation of gametes and embryos is now widely accepted. It is explicitly accepted in the Warnock Report. Now it is natural to take such donation to involve the surrender and transfer of all the donor's rights and duties in respect of any resulting child – rights and duties that the donor would otherwise have as the child's genetic parent. This is because a donation is a gift and normally if you give something away any rights and duties you have with respect to it are surrendered and transferred to the recipient of the gift.

This seems to imply an acceptance of two basic principles. These are first that the genetic parents are the initial holders of parental rights and duties as the producers of gametes; secondly that these rights and duties can be surrendered and transferred by the donation of gametes and embryos. It will be convenient to combine these into the single principle that gametes and embryos are transferable.

This principle lies unacknowledged behind many of the recommendations of the Warnock Report, for example the recommendations that donors should lose all rights and duties with respect to the child and that the woman who gives birth to a child from a donated egg, or embryo, should be considered to be its true mother. But it does not support the Warnock view that the woman who gives birth to the child in gestatory surrogacy is the child's true mother. On the contrary it supports the intuitive idea that in gestatory surrogacy the child belongs to the commissioning parents, the embryo *not* having been donated to the surrogate.

Let us now return to the genetic surrogate who is impregnated with sperm from the husband of the commissioning couple. As she gives birth to a child produced naturally from her own egg most people would agree that she must be its true mother. Under existing laws she is the child's legal mother but the child is illegitimate. However the position of the commissioning couple is problematic. As the genetic surrogate is impregnated with sperm from the husband of the commissioning couple, under present law he is in the same position as the natural father of any illegitimate child. Yet morally he seems to have a stronger claim to the child. This is because he supplied his sperm with the understanding that the child would be handed over for him and his wife to rear as their own.

The important point is not simply that he supplied his sperm, but that there was also a certain understanding or agreement. Genetic surrogacy is possible without the commissioning husband supplying the sperm. For example, the surrogate could be impregnated with sperm from a donor. In that case, if the commissioning parents have a claim to the child it derives entirely from the surrogacy agreement.

There is a question of whether any surrogacy agreement, in which the surrogate agrees to hand the child over to the commissioning parents when it is born, should be binding or enforceable. The prevailing view seems to be that none would be and none should be. The Warnock Committee says that all surrogacy agreements should be illegal and unenforceable. However, as we have seen, a good case could be made for allowing gestatory surrogacy and therefore for allowing some recognition of gestatory surrogacy agreements. We have also seen that certain principles that underlie many of the Warnock recommendations would support the view that in gestatory surrogacy the child belongs to the commissioning parents. Furthermore we shall see shortly that these same principles have some bearing on other forms of surrogacy.

The basic difficulty with surrogacy agreements can be seen most clearly if we imagine a married couple agreeing, or contracting, to have a child in the normal way by sexual intercourse for another couple. This can be called 'total' surrogacy. Total surrogacy is the most extreme form of surrogacy possible in which the man and woman who produce the child, the surrogate parents, perform all the functions of reproduction. Obviously there would be no (direct) genetic link between the child and the commissioning parents in total surrogacy.

The idea of total surrogacy raises many problems. Some people will find it totally repellent. However I do not put it forward as a practical possibility. On the contrary there are probably good reasons why it should not be a feature of institutionalised surrogacy. None the less it is of considerable theoretical interest because it displays the essential nature of the surrogacy agreement more clearly than other forms do. If the commissioning couple have any claim at all to the child in total surrogacy, it must be entirely because of the surrogacy agreement as nothing else is relevant.

The essence of the agreement is that the child will be handed over to the commissioning parents for them to raise as their own. However they could not hope to become its legal parents under existing law, except by adopting the child. This raises a fundamental difficulty because private adoptions are illegal. A child can be adopted only if a court makes an adoption order and it is clear that no court could allow a surrogacy agreement to pre-empt the question whether an adoption order should be made. For one thing an adoption requires the agreement of the natural parents, and it is laid down in the Children Act 1975 that the natural mother's agreement is 'ineffective' if given before six weeks after the birth of the child.[3] So obviously she could not be bound by an agreement made before the child was even conceived. Secondly the court is bound by the principle that the child's interests must be placed first.

Built into adoption law is the principle that parents cannot freely divest themselves of their parental rights and duties and transfer them elsewhere – or in short, the principle that children are not transferable. This principle, that children are not transferable, is deeply rooted in our moral thinking and lies at the heart of many objections to surrogacy arrangements. Without arguing for the principle I shall assume it is one that we embrace.

It seems to follow directly from this principle that total surrogacy and genetic surrogacy must be ruled out, for they both seem to involve the idea that the child when born is to be transferred to the commissioning parents. However the principle does not exclude gestatory surrogacy because the child already belongs to the commissioning parents in this case and does not need to be transferred to them except in a purely physical sense. Although the embryo is transferred to the uterus of the gestatory surrogate for gestation it is not donated to her and does not become her child.

Some people might want to accept the conclusion that gestatory surrogacy alone should be allowed and not total surrogacy or genetic surrogacy. However we cannot leave the matter there. Although genetic and total surrogacy both seem to violate the principle that children are not transferable it is arguable that really they do not. It is only because we assume that in these cases the child belongs to the surrogate mother rather than to the commissioning parents that we think that the principle of non-transferability is breached. Without this assumption there could be no question of the child having to be transferred. However this assumption is open to question. We have seen that the Warnock rule, that the woman who gives birth to the child is its mother, does not always hold. We have also seen that the donation of eggs or embryos results in a surrender and transference of the donor's parental rights and duties. Clearly then, our picture of genetic surrogacy and total surrogacy would change if they could be taken to involve the donation of the surrogate's egg or embryo to the commissioning parents. If that were the case the child would have to be considered to belong to the commissioning parents.

In these cases however there is the difficulty that neither the egg nor the embryo is removed from the woman's body. So if she donates them it must be while they remain intact in her body. I shall call this donation *in utero*.

Is donation *in utero* possible? At first sight it seems bizarre, perhaps absurd, to suppose that a woman might donate her egg or embryo without it being taken from her body with the result that the child she gestates does not belong to her. There is the double difficulty of supposing both that the child does not belong to the surrogate while she gestates it and that it already belongs to the commissioning parents. But these 'difficulties' are both features of gestatory surrogacy without being a problem there. Another factor to set aside is the tendency to think of the donation as essentially involving a physical transference or movement of the egg or embryo. All that is essential is that there should be a transference of rights and duties in respect of it.

There is no logical incoherence in the notion of *in utero* donation. The idea that an egg or embryo might be donated without being removed from the woman's body makes perfectly good sense. However there could be a question of whether the rules, conventions and laws of society allow anything to count as *in utero* donation. A comparison with child donation might make this clearer. The notion of child donation is not logically incoherent but nothing *counts* as the donation of a child in our society because nothing is allowed to do so. However, concerning gametes and embryos, we have already accepted the principle that they can be donated so it is difficult to see what basis there could be for rejecting the idea that they might be donated *in utero*.

Recognition and acceptance of *in utero* donation would change the concept of surrogacy. Instead of a surrogate mother being understood, as at present, to be a woman who has her own child for the express purpose of giving it over to the commissioning parents, which would certainly seem to violate the principle that children are not transferable, a genetic surrogate would be described more correctly as a woman who donates her egg, or embryo, to the commissioning couple and provides the functions of gestation and birth for them. In total surrogacy the couple producing the child could be described correctly as donating their gametes or their embryo to the commissioning parents, the wife providing the functions of gestation and birth for them. In gestatory surrogacy the surrogate supplies only the functions of gestation and birth. We see then that what is essential to surrogacy is the provision of the functions of gestation and birth. Under this new concept of surrogacy the child belongs to the commissioning parents in all cases and not to the woman who gestates and gives birth to it.

If embryos can be donated *in utero* we must draw a line between embryos which can be donated and foetuses or children which cannot be donated. Unless a clear line can be drawn, the principle that embryos can be donated and the principle that children cannot be donated will come into conflict.

This issue is too large to discuss in detail here. However it seems clear that the necessary distinction cannot be made in terms of the development of the embryo or foetus. Therefore the only rational and reasonably practical place to draw the line is before conception. A clear and simple rule would be that embryos can be donated only by agreements entered into at a point clearly before conception. This would fit with our general understanding of surrogacy, that is, that the surrogate agrees to do what she does before the pregnancy is under way. It is not an objection to the rule that the embryo does not exist before conception. However for most practical purposes surrogacy could be considered to involve the donation of gametes rather than embryos if donation is to take place before conception.

This analysis allows us to make a clear distinction between surrogacy and adoption. It is not only that surrogacy, on this understanding, does not involve a transference of the child from one set of parents to another. It is also that whereas the primary purpose of adoption is to provide for existing children who need parents, the essential aim of surrogacy is to bring children into existence for parents who want them. This means that in important respects parenthood by surrogacy is closer to normal parenthood than adoption can be. It retains to some degree the element of creation – the idea that but for the parents, the commissioning parents, the child would not have existed. Furthermore, depending on the form of surrogacy involved, there can be a genetic link between the surrogacy (or commissioning) parents and the child. Consequently surrogacy could provide a closer approximation to normal parenthood than adoption. Certainly it would be more appropriate as a solution to infertility.

If surrogacy is to have an acceptable place in society it will need the benefit of regulative institutions just as adoption does. But the danger is that because surrogacy is commonly thought of as necessarily involving adoption it will be institutionalised within the framework of the existing institutions and philosophy of adoption. If the argument of this paper is correct it would be better for the institutions supporting surrogacy to have a separate identity.

Surrogacy agreements are usually thought of as private arrangements between individuals drawn up by lawyers. It would be better for them to have a standard form regulated by law. It should be a legal requirement that people engaging in surrogacy should officially register a Surrogacy Agreement so that when the child is born the commissioning parents can be entered automatically in the records as its legal parents.

Certain conditions would need to be satisfied before a Surrogacy Agreement could be officially registered. There might be a requirement that surrogates and commissioning parents should receive counselling, that the surrogate satisfies certain criteria of suitability and so on. Some people would think there should also be conditions concerning the suitability of commissioning parents. I shall have more to say about that shortly.

We have already seen that the Surrogacy Agreement must be entered into at a point clearly before conception. However it is not envisaged that the surrogate should be subjected to tests to establish that she is not already pregnant. A simple requirement that a specified interval should elapse between the registration of the agreement and the birth of the child would be enough. The idea is that the commissioning parents could not be recognised and registered as the child's legal parents unless the requirement was met. Perhaps twelve months would be a long enough period. A forced delay between registering the Surrogacy Agreement and starting the pregnancy would be unlikely to cause hardship to either side provided it was not too long. On the other hand it would be reasonable to allow the surrogate some time to reconsider and possibly withdraw from the Surrogacy Agreement before finally committing herself and starting the pregnancy.

This brings us to one of the most vexed questions concerning surrogacy. To what extent is the surrogate to be bound by the Surrogacy Agreement? In particular, might she be compelled to give up the child if she decides that she wants to keep it?

Some people believe that it would always be wrong to compel a surrogate mother to release the child even though she has entered into an agreement to do so. The most plausible ground for this belief is that such compulsion is likely to cause the surrogate unacceptable suffering and distress, taking into account the special physical and psychological state of a woman who has just given birth to a child.

My first thoughts are that such compulsion would not feature as much as is feared in a properly instituted system of surrogacy. By careful screening and counselling it should be possible to reduce the risk of surrogates changing their minds about giving up the child. Obviously they need to be physically and psychologically robust women with adequate self-knowledge for the task. With time, shifts in general modes of thought and attitudes might make it less likely that surrogates will feel unable to give up the child as it comes to be accepted that a surrogacy child belongs to the commissioning parents and not to the surrogate mother. None the less there might still be some surrogates who want to keep the child. We need to know whether the above theory requires that they should be compelled to release it.

It would be consistent with the broadly contractual approach of the theory to make some provision in the Surrogacy Agreement to meet this eventuality.[4] Various escape clauses would be possible. The simplest, which would do most to meet the objection, would be the provision that the surrogate can keep the child if she wants to. I am not convinced that such a generous protection for the surrogate would be needed nor that it could be justified. However it could be incorporated into the Surrogacy Agreement without disturbing the main lines of the theory. The escape clause would make no difference in the normal case where the child is handed over to the commissioning parents. In these cases the child could still be registered automatically as their child with all that this entails. That is the essential importance of the agreement rather than any supposed guarantee it offers that the child will be surrendered. But of course the clause would make the commissioning parents vulnerable.

Allowing the surrogate to keep the child simply if she wants to would be very hard on the commissioning parents and could be quite unfair to them. The reason for saying, in the first place, that it would be wrong to compel surrogates to release the child is that to do so might cause them extreme distress. The suggested escape clause would allow the surrogate to keep the child for any reason such as that her own young children say they would like a baby sister or brother, or out of spite. This would be manifestly unfair to the commissioning parents because they too are liable to suffer considerable distress and to feel a strong sense of injustice if the child is withheld.

It would be unjust to allow the surrogate to withhold the child unreasonably. The test of unreasonableness in this case would be largely whether the surrogate is likely to suffer unacceptable distress if the child is taken from her. If it is plain that she would not suffer such distress if the child was removed her refusal to release it would be unreasonable. This puts the onus on the commissioning parents to show that the surrogate would not suffer by removal of the child. It might be better to put the burden of proof on the surrogate and say that she should be allowed to keep the child only if compelling her to release it would cause her unacceptable distress. Wherever the burden of proof is placed this revised provision implies that a surrogate could be compelled to release the child, if she withholds it unreasonably. A provision along these lines would be a reasonable safeguard for the surrogate while giving due recognition to the dangers for the commissioning parents. Of course some machinery for (legally) transferring the child to the surrogate in cases where she is to keep it would be needed.

Finally I shall examine one further problem. Surrogacy is sometimes condemned on the grounds that it could have bad consequences for the child. In particular it is sometimes suggested that surrogacy parents might endanger the child and therefore that access to surrogacy should be regulated and controlled. This takes surrogacy towards adoption and suggests that prospective surrogacy parents like prospective adopters should be investigated for their suitability.

There is something outrageous in the suggestion that a childless couple who seek surrogacy as a solution to their infertility should be screened and vetted to see whether they are morally and socially fit to be parents. If it were not for some accident of nature, some physical disability, they would be free to procreate like anyone else. There is no control over who has a child by natural reproduction. Nor do we think there should be. So why should there be control over access to surrogacy?

The right to procreate is often said to be a basic human right. What exactly it amounts to is a difficult question. Presumably it rules out compulsory sterilisation. In 1976 a court refused to allow an eleven-year-old mentally retarded girl to be sterilised on the grounds that it is 'the right of a woman to reproduce'.[5] It appears then that the right is not subject to a condition of fitness for parenthood nor to the qualification that reproduction should be in the interests of the resulting child.

If there is a right to reproduce it could be argued that doctors who withhold treatment for infertility on non-medical grounds, even in the interests of the child, violate the rights of their patients. In principle it is not for doctors to decide who should reproduce any more than it is for them to decide who should live or die. Nor is it for social workers or for the state to decide this, or philosophers.

None the less it would be irresponsible of doctors to provide treatment for infertility if it was plain that to do so would result in the birth of a seriously damaged or handicapped child or if the parents are manifestly incapable of looking after a child. If there is seriously debilitating hereditary disease, severe drug addiction or if the intending parents are severely handicapped and totally incapable of bringing up a child a doctor may feel that she has a duty not to make it possible for them to have a child. There are dangers here because such cases involve judgment. However it is inescapable that there will be cases where existing infertility might be considered a fortunate 'act of nature' which the doctor has no duty to correct. A not unreasonable principle for such cases might be: 'Thou shalt not sterilise but needst not strive officiously to fertilise.'

Most people would probably agree that if it is obvious and demonstrable that fertility treatment could only result in the production of a severely handicapped child, or even a seriously disadvantaged child, the treatment might be withheld. But they would think it wrong if people ordinarily seeking a remedy for infertility by fertility drugs, artificial insemination, *in vitro* fertilisation, embryo transfer or donation of gametes or embryos were subjected to screening and vetting for general fitness for parenthood. Apart from possibly being intrusive such a procedure would bring their right to reproduce into question.

If surrogacy is sought as a remedy for infertility there is no reason why it should not be regarded in the same light as other methods of alleviating infertility as far as access to it is concerned. As with these other treatments there might be obviously demonstrable cases where surrogacy must be refused. However, those cases apart, people seeking surrogacy could object to screening for moral, social and general fitness on the grounds that it violates their right to reproduce. They could claim that they have as much right as anyone else to procreate and an equal right with other seekers to surrogacy.

Prospective adopters are in a completely different position. They cannot claim a right to adopt. This might seem odd, particularly if they are seeking adoption as a solution to childlessness caused by infertility. But of course there is a difference. In adoption the child already exists and has to be taken into account as a person with interests, as an end in itself. Indeed the child's interests are paramount. This is incompatible with the idea that particular adopters have a right to adopt or have as much right as anyone else to adopt. They may adopt only if it would be in the best interests of the child.

The principle that the child's interests are paramount cannot apply to surrogacy or to other treatments for infertility in the same way as it does to adoption. We can ask with respect to an existing child whether this or that would be in its best interests. But if the child is not yet conceived this would make no sense.

The upshot of these considerations seems to be that there should be only minimal regulation or control over who has access to surrogacy – no more than is ordinarily exercised by doctors in the provision of fertility treatments and certainly less than exists for adoption. This assumes of course that surrogacy is tied to the idea of relief for infertility. The importance of this is that it preserves the connection between surrogacy and parenthood. The connection with parenthood is the overriding consideration that should guide any extensions of surrogacy beyond the strict limits of relief for infertility. No doubt some extensions beyond these limits could be justified. But there is a danger that surrogacy could become a source of supply of infants for whatever purpose. Perhaps the main controls should be concerned with preventing that from happening and with preserving the connection between surrogacy and parenthood.

## Postscript

Following the Warnock Report legislation was enacted in 1985 to make commercial surrogacy illegal in Britain. A further bill (Surrogacy Arrangements (Amendment) Bill 1985) which seeks to stop all surrogacy, commercial or not, is now (1986) before the House of Lords, introduced by the Earl of Halsbury. If this bill is enacted the 'Warnock rule' will become law. Most of the peers speaking to the bill take it for granted that the woman who bears the child should be considered to be its legal mother. The bill is very likely to be passed by the House of Lords but it is unlikely that the government will give it time in the House of Commons.

Meanwhile in America the world's first gestatory surrogate, Shannon Boff, gave birth to a baby girl in Ann Arbor, Michigan in April 1986. A few weeks before the birth of the baby the surrogacy agent, lawyer Noel P. Keane, promoter and pioneer of commercial surrogacy in America, secured a circuit court ruling that the commissioning parents and not the surrogate mother who gave birth to it would be the child's legal parents and that their names, not the surrogate's name, should appear on the birth certificate. The judge made the ruling subject to medical tests to establish that the commissioning parents were the child's genetic parents.

## Notes

1  *Report of the Committee of Inquiry into Human Fertilisation and Embryology* (1984)
   Cmnd. 9314. London, HMSO; repr. in Mary Warnock (1985), *A Question of Life*
   with Introduction and Conclusion by Mary Warnock. Oxford, Blackwell.
2  cf. Edgar Page (1985), 'Donation, surrogacy and adoption', *Journal of Applied
   Philosophy*, 2 (2), for a fuller discussion of some of the main lines of the theory.
3  cf. M. D. A. Freeman (1976), *The Children Act 1975: text with concise commentary*.
   London, Sweet & Maxwell, 12.6.
4  I owe this to Dilys Page and Uma Narayan who independently suggested it to me
5  'Re. D (a Minor) [1976]', 1 All ER 326; mentioned in *Human Procreation* (1984),
   Council of Science and Society Report. Oxford, p. 63.

# 11 Needs and justice in health resource allocation

*Rod Sheaff*

Who should receive health care and who should not? The obvious way to take this is as a question of distributive justice. But although this approach has the attraction of building upon philosophical work outside medical ethics, it is fraught with difficulties. Even writers who use the concept of justice to address issues of health resource allocation recognise that ill health is not of itself an injustice. Principles of justice bear on such issues only indirectly, by bearing upon the social measures to deal with ill health.[1] To understand the normative aspects of health resource allocation we first require some conclusions about such questions as the nature of health care, the resources it requires and how to organise health services. The concept of 'need' is more likely than the concept of 'justice' to illuminate these matters. For the concept of need is both more concrete and determinate than that of justice and easier to relate to health concerns. The concept of need has the added interest of figuring conspicuously in public and political debate about health resources. It has already received attention in the literature, to such effect that some writers now find it necessary to apologise for mentioning needs at all.[2] This chapter argues in favour of relying on the concept of need in debates about health resource allocation rather than on the concept of justice and the concomitant concept of rights.

Summarising the questions a concept of need is to be used to answer can reveal what logical characteristics a concept of need suitable for addressing problems of health resource allocation will have. One set of questions concerns the criteria for allocating health resources between care groups. A second set concerns the ethically 'hard' questions about the criteria by which patients should be selected for expensive and scarce but life-saving medical techniques,[3] especially those which can maintain life but do nothing to improve its very poor quality. (Certain less costly procedures such as non-therapeutic abortion also generate ethically 'hard' questions.) The distinction between real resources and money raises a third set of ethical issues surrounding health resource allocation. They concern the organisational means by which health resources are rationed and allocated, produced and consumed. A normative theory of health resource allocation must illuminate these questions too.

If a concept of need is to be of use in clarifying, let alone resolving, these questions it should at least meet the following specifications. Practical, and in particular allocative, conclusions should follow from it. Yet the concept of need should beg as few normative issues as possible, for its use is partly to resolve debate. It should be defined in terms that make any moral assumptions it embodies explicit (so that those who apply the concept are forewarned); but if possible be non-moral altogether. The concept should also be applicable to conflicts of interest over health resource allocation, suggesting reasons for resolving conflicts in particular ways but without normatively preempting the issues. It should also enable us to identify and specify needs, to relate them to provision of the different sorts of health care, and enable priorities to be accorded among those services. It should at least generate some lexical, ordinal sequence of needs and distinguish needs from mere wants. But not just any theory of human needs will do provided it is explicit and uncontroversial; it must be relevant to the very particular and concrete concerns of clinical practice so that it can generate decisions in ethically difficult cases. The theory must be consistent with, or even draw upon, the clinical sciences.

We can swiftly discount a subjective concept of need.[4] It admits no public identification of needs and no means of allowing that people can ever be mistaken about their own needs (though they can still be mistaken about other people's needs). It precludes the possibility that physical or mental disorder could distort individuals' understanding of their needs; or that misinformation or ideology could. The subjective concept affords no workable basis for interpersonal comparisons of needs.

Of objective concepts of needs there are two varieties, the 'essentialist' and the biological. 'Essentialist' concepts of need have had much the wider philosophical attention. These concepts of need derive from a philosophical account of human nature.[5] The approach has the merit of focusing upon attributes and activities that are uniquely human and hence relevant to a theory of human health. Yet this is also a disadvantage for our present task. For the more mundane motives and activities that humans have in common with other animals are also a main concern of health services. At root the essentialist theories are a priori and arbitrary in the way that they ethically deprioritise the group of needs which humans share with other animals.

There remains what might be called a biological concept of need. Norman Daniels has offered a signpost towards such a concept.[6] But his theory requires further development. We can begin to develop it using the valid components of the concepts of need described above. Like Daniels let us start with a premiss that both health and natural needs are connected with normal species functioning. The latter we can see in biological terms as (first) individual survival and (secondly) reproduction; together with the relief of any incidental pains. Then natural needs can be ranked according to how long each natural need can be frustrated without physiological abnormality resulting. This length of time we can call the natural need's 'period of urgency'. Obviously satisfying sexual needs is optional in a way that satisfying individual survival needs is not. Satisfying individuals' survival needs is a precondition of satisfying the sexual needs and indeed of satisfying the non-natural needs too.

Besides the individual survival needs and the sexual needs a third category of natural needs is observable. These do not necessarily contribute to individual survival or the reproduction of the species. The third group of natural needs may arise adventitiously.[7] An important example for present purposes is the need to relieve pains, since that is generally held to be a main function of health care. While individual survival needs are more urgent than sexual ones, there is no a priori way to rank the urgency of the whole category of adventitious natural needs (such as pain relief) against the urgency of the other two categories (sexual and individual survival needs). For some adventitious natural needs do, while others do not, contribute to individual survival or reproduction; and among those that do the periods of urgency are sometimes of the same order of magnitude as the periods of urgency of the other natural needs.

Some adventitious natural needs apart, natural needs stand in a reciprocal relation to humans' biological life-cycle. That life-cycle can be conceptualised in practical terms (rather than in purely physiological or biochemical terms) as a cycle of having and actively satisfying natural needs. Natural needs are only ever satisfied temporarily while life remains. Exactly how temporarily, the period of urgency quantifies. But to have a natural need is one thing, to have it satisfied, quite another. The typical link between a (natural) need and its satisfaction is (as some essentialist theories observe) individuals' own activity. This activity ranges from reflex (for example breathing) to reflexes overlaid by conscious control and to the most conscious deliberate action (for example cultivating crops). (Of course not all reflexes are directly connected with natural needs.) Even those needs usually met by reflex become conscious, because of pain, if there is severe privation. For example we breathe by reflex but become quickly and painfully conscious of breathlessness should this reflex misfunction. This suggests a view of natural needs as a part of a cycle (which we can call the need cycle). Physiological stimuli, largely from within the body, motivate conscious action or stimulate reflex action. This action exercises the natural capacities which are discussed below.

For a natural need to be satisfied is therefore more than a subjective event of the original need-stimulus being temporarily quelled as a motive or stimulus to action. It is for specific physiological processes to occur so that the body is repaired and maintained or reproduced or freed of pain. To say that someone needs water is (in this sense) not logically equivalent to saying that he ought to get it. It is to make a brute-empirical comment either that he is subjectively motivated to get water; or that getting water is objectively necessary for him to survive or reproduce, to relieve pain or satisfy a non-natural need. Such descriptions can be made from a standpoint entirely external to any moral, or even any normative, standpoint. Whether from the speaker's standpoint or from the moral point of view he who needs water ought also to get it depends upon whether additional normative assumptions hold.

Acting upon natural needs exercises some or all of a person's natural capacities. The natural capacities range from reflex action to abstract thought. Any adult of normal intelligence is at least grossly aware of the capacities he uses in everyday life. They include several reflexes (for example breathing), continence, mobility, the ability to manipulate objects, the five senses and consciousness. These are the minimum natural capacities necessary to satisfy the natural needs entirely by one's own actions. But even Robinson Crusoe did not manage that; he had not only tools made by other people to help him but also the knowledge and skills commonly available in the England he had left. Solitary activity would be extremely atypical of the ways in which needs are satisfied. Many natural needs are satisfied with other people's help. To get this the capacity for speech, or failing that to communicate in other ways, is necessary. The act of enlisting someone else's help can be very minimal, for instance a croak for help, a gesture or grimace. It would appear that some capacities are less dispensable than others to the activities that satisfy the natural needs. Operational research into the activities of daily living would be required to discover which are more, and which less, dispensable.

Of the natural capacities, consciousness is central. It is the capacity that mediates needs and action, orientates the agent in regard to getting or making the objects that satisfy his natural needs. It is the capacity by which physical action is planned, controlled and coordinated, the capacity that can motivate action in response to environmental changes and opportunities to satisfy needs. It is necessary for communication by speech, hence important in achieving other people's acquiesence or cooperation in the agent's efforts to satisfy his needs. Consciousness is also central in that natural needs become conscious. If consciousness is impaired other people, among them health workers, know better than the affected individual what his individual survival needs are. Otherwise, and usually, the agent himself is likely to be the most competent judge of what his needs are and how to exercise his natural capacities to satisfy them. Permanent loss of consciousness is catastrophic to the natural need-cycle and to the satisfaction of non-natural needs.

Where the need cycle is impaired and the impaired parts cannot be restored or prosthetically replaced, a person will rely upon others' activity to satisfy the needs which previously he would have used his own action and natural capacities to satisfy. Others' activity substitutes for the impaired natural need-cycle, at least as far as individual survival needs, fertility and pain relief are concerned. Much health service activity consists in exactly this. So dependence, quantified perhaps by the labour time that others spend in substituting for the impaired parts of the need cycle, might serve as an index, if not a measure, of need-cycle impairment. How much of other people's labour time is required to substitute for the impaired parts of the need-cycle will depend upon the current state of health-care technologies. So if dependence is an index of need-cycle impairment, the extent of impairment caused by a given disease or injury (for example the severing of a limb, which microsurgical techniques can now repair in some cases) is historically contingent and variable.

Other needs remain – the historical needs such as the need for education or for personal transport. It can be argued – as Freud did – that all other needs develop through the activities that satisfy natural needs.[8] They arise sometimes as needs for the means to satisfy the natural needs and sometimes as acquired needs for the by-products of the process of satisfying the natural needs. This is a strong claim and elaborating it fully is beside our main task here. But one can illustrate the approach by considering the need for autonomy.[9] Our theory of needs would take the need for an autonomy as a non-natural need. If a person had a need for autonomy that would be because autonomy was a condition for satisfying one's natural – and many non-natural needs – in the person's social circumstances. Non-natural needs thus originate from a complex of factors including social relations, the agent's attempt to satisfy his natural needs, and his beliefs about the means to do so in the circumstances.

All this is relevant to health resource allocation for two reasons. First, a theory of historical needs would generate a much more specific account of the conditions under which consciousness, and the unconscious, come to function in ways which, according to the theory of natural needs, are unhealthy. That would clarify the distinction between functional and organic mental disorder.[10] It would also clarify the distinction between curing mental disease and socially controlling deviancy. The second distinction is relevant to deciding what resource should be allocated to mental health services.

Secondly a person meets both historical and natural needs by exercising his natural capacities. Maintaining one's natural capacitie bears directly upon one's ability to meet both one's natural and one' historical needs. Suppose that 'quality of life', in the normative sense o the phrase, depends upon the ability to satisfy not only natural need but at least some of the historical needs too and to exercise one' acquired and natural capacities. If so, maintaining the natural capacitie has a direct influence upon a person's quality of life.

Natural and historical needs both provide motives for preventing and curing disease, handicap, pain and trauma. The remedies, where they exist, consist in restoring the impaired parts of the natural need-cycle by restoring the physiological functions and structures that comprise natural needs and capacities. Failing that it may be possible to replace the impaired functions and structures prosthetically. If that fails it only remains for the sufferer to live as best he can with the impaired natura need-cycle or for someone else's activity to substitute for his own activity in the need-cycle. Nowadays these tasks fall largely to health services. From the user's standpoint the function of health resources is a means to enable the need-cycle to continue.

From this standpoint being healthy is to possess all the natural need and capacities of a person of one's own age, race and sex; to be able to survive (and during early and middle adulthood reproduce) by satisfying the natural needs; and all this without pains. On this view of health ageing and childbearing do not count as unhealthy *per se*. They only necessitate health care in so far as these processes may incidentally impair the need-cycle or be painful. If health is especially important that is because disease, handicap, pain and trauma have far-reaching effects upon satisfying both natural and historical needs; that is, upon the quality of life.

A concept of health implies criteria for effectiveness in the use of health resources to maintain a person's health. Health resources are used effectively in so far as their use increases the recipient's ability to sustain his need-cycle and to do so painlessly. Health resource use is effective whenever this increase results, and only if it results. Achieving it may require health resources for other purposes than intervening in a patient's natural need-cycles only. Satisfying historical needs may directly influence the prospects for physical recovery. Feeling better may be a psychological precondition of getting physically – not to say mentally – healthier.[11]

Two sorts of evidence would indicate how effectively health resources had been used; occurrences of pains and incidence of need-cycle impairments. The occurrence of pains is discovered simply by asking the alleged sufferers, with behavioural evidence offering circumstantial corroboration. For the individual survival needs, need-cycle impairment is practically overcome to the extent that a person can actively satisfy his natural needs. This involves more than being able to exercise one's natural capacities. It includes having the motivation or stimulus to initiate need-satisfying action. (The incidence of self-neglect would be an indicator of the former.) The action taken must also be likely to satisfy the natural need producing it. Moreover the agent must be in such a physical condition that the effects of the action would indeed conduce to individual survival or reproduction. For instance a seriously diabetic child might have a great desire for sweets. Although his action would be motivated by the natural need of hunger the diabetes might make the effects of eating sweets fatal. For this child to be able to survive by satisfying his hunger in this way requires not only the sweet itself but a cure for his diabetes.

The incidence of untreated but treatable need-cycle impairments and of relievable pains among a population is (on the arguments above) evidence of the insufficient use of health resources. Incidence of untreatable need-cycle impairment and of untreatable pains is evidence of the ineffectiveness of existing clinical techniques. Among people of working age, return to the workforce (which includes the unemployment register) would be a main indicator of the restoration of the need-cycle. Among people older or younger than working age self-care in a social setting outside the health system – in the 'community' as the current euphemism has it – would be a corresponding indicator. A health system whose clinical techniques were completely effective and which applied sufficient resources to cure all treatable need-cycle impairment and pains would make itself redundant except for preventive care, curing accidental pains and traumas, and easing the passages into life (for both mother and child) and out of it.

Advances in medical technology make some diseases clinically manageable at the cost of making them ethically difficult. Techniques which replace the patient's own activities in satisfying his individual survival needs are increasingly available but not techniques for making that substitution unnecessary by restoring the patient's natural capacities. Life is maintained but its quality is very poor. For instance radical surgery and intensive nursing might postpone somebody's death from a degenerative disease only to leave him completely dependent, utterly paralysed and just conscious enough to be aware only of excruciating pain. To apply the criterion of effectiveness would imply that health resources should be withdrawn whenever, but only when, the activity of having individual survival needs and acting upon them (even minimally) has broken down comprehensively and irretrievably. Then health resources no longer support a self-sustaining cycle of needing and acting but completely substitute for it. Where needing or acting have entirely been replaced by health resources a residue of physiological functions may proceed intact. Some brain-stem activity might continue and the blood still circulate, for example, even in a patient who had irretrievably lost consciousness, the ability to breathe unaided and so on. But the remaining functions would have lost any effect upon the patient's need-cycle. Using health resources to maintain that residual function no longer assists him in creating the conditions for his own survival. The criteria we derived above would count it an ineffective use of health resources to maintain these residual functions alone. The patient's need-cycle has already ceased irrevocably. Withdrawing the support for what physiological processes remain will not alter this.

There remains the question whether any less comprehensive substitution of health-care resources for a patient's own natural needs, activities and capacities would count as ineffective health resource use. In one important circumstance it might. Consider the cases of Elaine Esporito and Karen Quinlan. Both had irretrievably lost consciousness but not reflexive activity.[12] In so far as a person can be unconscious of her needs (and satisfy them reflexively), and in so far as reflexes qualify as actions, it might appear an effective use of health resources to restore the reflex actions when they fail. However this is to take too restricted a view of the activity involved in the need-cycle. We have seen that this cycle requires conscious action if it is to be self-sustaining in the long term.

As in the previous cases residual physiological processes operate but without practical effect in enabling the patient to create her own conditions of survival even by the most minimal conscious action. So irretrievable loss of consciousness would be a reason for ceasing to use health resources because that use would be ineffective.

At the opposite extreme are circumstances in which health resources are often used but are unnecessary for health as we have defined it. The Princess of Wales's cosmetic surgery is a trivial example; the recently reported use of radical mastectomy as a preventive measure a horrific one. Clinical interventions may be available, even technically successful, but their effect is not to maintain or restore a person's ability to need, to act upon his or her needs and to survive or reproduce or avoid pain by satisfying those needs. These uses of health resources too are ineffective, because superfluous.

It is not necessarily a sign of ill health that someone uses his natural capacities to satisfy his needs in dangerous, eccentric or immoral ways. Someone who steals from Oxfam or writes a book to demonstrate that he is God is not, on our account of health and needs, sick. In this respect consciousness and conscious action are natural capacities like any others. Dangerous, eccentric or immoral actions would only be unhealthy if they were bound to fail to satisfy the natural need motivating them or to impair the cycle of needing, acting and surviving or reproducing by satisfying the natural needs. (So on this view alcoholism or drug addiction would count as ill-health.) Otherwise our theory would count such behaviours as repeated stealing or publishing odd beliefs as deviancy not disease. Mental handicap and organic mental illness the theory conceptualises as it does physical illness or handicap. If there are valid reasons to use health resources upon social deviants they are criminological or political reasons, not grounds of the deviant's health.

The concept of health as the painless, self-sustaining activity of having and satisfying natural needs also counts as ineffective, the use of health resources in ways that would tend to make the recipients less likely to exercise their natural capacities for themselves. It implies that health resources are used ineffectively where recipients can care for themselves, at the point at which institutionalisation sets in.

Our theory also counts it as ineffective resource use to provide non-therapeutic care (for example hospital 'hotel' services) that patients can undertake for themselves, or to compensate for the deficiencies of society at large in providing other means for people to obtain food, shelter, companionship and so on.[13] Institutionalisation extends beyond hospital 'hotel' services to the point where active health maintenance is abdicated by the population to the health system, which then treats the effects of patients' inactivity. Using resources to produce this sort of institutionalisation would also fail our test for effectiveness. But once the damage was done there would remain a case for using health resources to remedy it, if effective remedy existed.

The health resources necessary for providing health care according to these need-based criteria can in principle be quantified. This poses two further questions. In terms of the need theory above, a health system is allocatively efficient to the extent that health resources are allocated to everybody upon whom those resources can be used effectively, and to nobody else. This raises the question of what organisational forms of health system are likely to have the highest allocative efficiency. The other question arises in the event of failure to produce or obtain the necessary resources. It is the question of how to allocate resources that fall short of the level implied by the need-based criteria. The answers lead full circle back to the concept of distributive justice.

Allocative efficiency requires two conditions. One is that the people upon whom health resources can effectively be used are identified. The other is that the necessary quantities and types of resources reach these people and them only. So health system 'gatekeepers' have two tasks. One is to discover whether a person's condition is amenable to the effective use of health resources for prevention, cure or care. If it is, the patient must be given access to the health resources that he instrumentally needs, the resources necessary and sufficient to restore health as far as possible.

Whether patient or health worker initiates the process, allocative efficiency requires a minimum of obstacles to mutual access between health services and the population they serve. Obstacles are of three main kinds. Sheer scarcity of health resources we shall return to later. Logistic obstacles consist in physical inaccessibility of health resources because of the times and places at which these resources are made available, or ignorance that health resources are available. Third – and most relevant here – are organisational obstacles. They exist when, to get health care, a person must satisfy social criteria unconnected with his health status and to the effectiveness of health care resources. Such social criteria include race, nationality, organisational membership, place of residence or possessing money. The latter is a notorious reason why markets in health care may prove allocatively inefficient.

Note that on the theory advanced here that is an empirical claim. The concept of need is not *inherently* inimical to markets. It might be true, although paradoxical, that in practice markets had a higher allocative efficiency than any other method of organisation. Our theory of needs provides logically independent criteria for judging the allocative efficiency of health systems. If, as many writers suspect, markets in health care are not allocatively very efficient, that would suggest not that the concept of needs is inherently prejudicial towards markets but that markets are prejudicial to the task of allocating health resources according to need-based criteria.

At the individual level our theory yields a criterion of urgency. Each individual survival need admits of frustration only for a determinate period of urgency. Within the period of urgency it is necessary to restore the impaired natural capacity to meet the need or replace that capacity artificially, or substitute for the impaired capacity by having someone else meet the natural need for the sufferer.

This criterion might imply a different sequence for treating a given list of patients than the criterion of prioritising those patients for whom health resources could produce the biggest improvement in the quality of life; a different sequence than, say, the priorities suggested by using QALYs (Quality Adjusted Life Years). Instead the criterion outlined here would prioritise the patients who faced the most immediate *loss* of quality of life, through impairment of their ability to satisfy their natural and historical needs or through the loss of life itself, if health care resources were not made available. This suggests that among a group of users resources should first be allocated to those to whom the shortest period of urgency remains, provided that the resources can be used effectively. Thereafter resources should be allocated in order of decreasing urgency until they are exhausted. Then a waiting list, still in order of urgency, would be required (and periodically reviewed as individuals' conditions, and hence remaining period of urgency, changed). This criterion would obviously give high priority to effective life-saving uses of health resources and to the prevention of handicap. Less obviously it would also give a higher priority to health promotion and preventive care than to treating people whose disability, although treatable, had stabilised.

The criterion may be clear but its criteriology would be complex. Disease, injuries and handicaps rarely correspond one-to-one with natural needs or capacities, often affecting many at once. In that case the shortest of the several periods of urgency left for each sufferer would be the criterion for resource allocation. Even for similar diseases or injuries the remaining period of urgency will vary with the circumstances and individuals' physiological robustness. So we may not conclude that (say) everyone with effectively treatable cardio-respiratory damage should have priority in receiving resources over anyone with gastric disorders. Assessing the remaining periods of urgency is a technical clinical judgment. Period of urgency is a quantifiable criterion for health resource allocation. Time – that is, the duration of life of present quality left to sufferers if there be no intervention – is the unit of measurement and ranking.

This method can only work if the scarcity is moderate. If health resources are so scarce that individual ranking by urgency will still commit far more resources than exist, it becomes necessary to prioritise between whole categories of patient.

Our need theory regards health resources as a means for service users to regain or retain their natural capacities to meet their natural needs, thereby to be able to survive (and, at certain times of life, reproduce) painlessly. This suggests an allocative criterion of minimising need-cycle impairment in a population as the global counterpart of the criterion of effectiveness in clinical intervention. (If a society were capable of mobilising the human resources restored by effective health resource use, minimising incapacity would also help relieve some of the original resource scarcity.) But assuming it is prudent to minimise need-cycle impairment, what might the phrase mean and what allocative criteria might it imply? Three criteria suggest themselves: numbers of people with need-cycle impairment; total duration of their need-cycle impairments; and severity of need-cycle impairment.

We can rank these criteria if we make one more assumption. It is that illness occurs randomly. Then it would be prudent from each person's standpoint to allocate health resources so as to minimise the number of people likely to have impaired need-cycles. Resources would first be allocated to the commonest effectively preventable and treatable conditions, then in decreasing order of care group size until resources are all committed. On this basis treating arthritis would be higher priority than treating AIDS (at least, until one could reliably predict that without intervention AIDS would become more common than arthritis). The rationale is simple. The commoner a disease the more probable that any given individual will suffer it.

If several diseases, injuries or conditions were equally common a tie-breaking criterion would be required. How much a condition impairs a person's need-cycles depends upon both its duration and its severity. An index of these would be the quantity of resources necessary, both inside and outside the health system, to substitute by human or mechanical aid for the impaired parts of the need-cycle. Then the tie-breaking criterion would be to allocate resources to the care group where intervention would save the most resources otherwise becoming necessary to meet the sufferers' individual survival needs. But this supposes that such a quantity, abstracting over the duration and the severity of an impairment, is measurable. It only is on some very strong economic assumptions. If the quantification is impossible, duration of need-cycle impairment alone would become the tie-breaking criterion. Preventing the longest episodes of incapacity will both minimise the average duration of interruption to the sufferers' own need-cycle and soonest free resources for other uses. Severity of need-cycle impairment remains as the third tie-breaking criterion should the other two prove inconclusive. This ranking is likely to favour preventive care if that is cheaper or more effective than cure in limiting need-cycle impairment. The ranking is similarly likely to prioritise cure over care.

We have assumed that ill health strikes at random. This is not always so. Populations at particular risk have been identified for many diseases. When resources are scarce relative to need-based criteria, this fact generates conflicts of interest over health resource allocation. Organisational questions also generate such conflicts. Allocative efficiency by need-based criteria might require a non-market health system; maximising doctors' incomes might require a market. Assuming that allocative efficiency is in health system users' interests, there is a conflict of interests between health system users and some health care professionals.

This is where moral considerations are raised, usually as claims about rights to health care (or at least, to the protection of one's health) and about distributive justice.[14] Scarcity and conflicting interests seem to underscore the point that simply having an instrumental need for health resources does not imply any right to have that need satisfied.[15]

We can now relate our findings about need-based health resource allocation to the concept of justice and its correlative concept of rights.

Debate on how to characterise the functions, meanings and uses of these moral concepts continues interminably. Yet underlying it is a remarkable degree of consensus about at least two main features of the concept of justice. One is that it at least involves a definite procedure for making practical decisions. 'Justice' is a formal concept in the sense of being at a high level of generality. Most of the empirical data required for ascertaining the substantive claims of justice have to be supplied by non-moral theories; in the present case knowledge of epidemiology, health system organisation, resource availability and so on. The other widely agreed feature of the concept of justice is that justice consists, at least, in considering, and applying reciprocally acceptable standards to, the interests of every party to a conflict.

Suppose this sort of procedure can yield determinate practical conclusions about health resource allocation. Either the concept of justice will yield identical allocative results to our need-based criteria or it will not. If the allocative conclusions of the two approaches coincided neither need-theorist nor moralist could complain. Each could allege the other theory as a secondary support for their own. Then the choice between the two approaches would depend, not on substantive, but upon epistemological and other secondary grounds. But if theories of distributive justice and the need criteria yield different substantive results one can either sacrifice justice in the interest of needs or vice versa.

In applying the concept of justice enough is done if an allocation is found that each party to the conflict can accept in the circumstances. Typically the result will be a compromise by which no one's requirement for health resources (in terms of need-based criteria) is met fully. The conflict of interests and its causes remain, contained but otherwise undisturbed because the concept of justice simply takes them for granted. Rather than be content with allocating scarcity equitably it is for most people more prudent to recognise the unsatisfactory aspects of such an outcome so that the causes of the conflict or scarcity can be identified and if possible removed. Using the theory of natural needs is more likely to expose the fact of conflict, its causes and remedies. If such remedies were achieved the 'circumstances of justice' would no longer obtain.[16] But criteria for allocating the now sufficient health resources would still be required. Only the theory of needs would remain applicable. To borrow a clinical metaphor, of the two approaches to conflicts over health resource allocation theories of justice are only a palliative response. A theory of need is likelier to yield a diagnosis and identify any available cure.

So there are advantages in using a theory of need rather than a theory of distributive justice as a medium for decisions about health resource allocation. Compared with a theory of distributive justice a theory of needs discovers rather than disguises conflicts and their causes. For theories of justice address the task of containing, not explaining or removing, social conflict. The concept of need has epistemological advantages in terms of empirical verifiability and objectivity. It is more readily applicable both to organisational issues and to clinical decisions. If some of its substantive conclusions about allocating scarce resources seem chilling, the fault is not in the theory of natural needs. It lies in whatever causes resource scarcity and the ineffectiveness of some clinical techniques. So where needs and the claims of justice conflict there are epistemological and normative reasons to prefer the claims of needs. This will not necessarily prevent us from raising other considerations in areas where the need-based criteria imply that there are no *health* reasons to deploy health resources. Non-therapeutic abortion or cosmetic surgery might nevertheless be defensible for aesthetic, social or other reasons.

Here we reach the boundaries of theories of health provision. But we have at least found some prima-facie reasons to think that the concept of needs can be developed in directions that provide clear empirical criteria for health resource allocation. Further ethical research is required to assess and exploit that potential.

## Notes

1  Plant, R. (1978), 'Gifts, exchanges and the political economy of health; ii: How should health care be distributed?' *Journal of Medical Ethics*, iv, 1, p. 8.

2  For example, Doyal, L. and Gough, I. (1984), 'A theory of human needs', *Critical Social Theory*, x, p. 6f.

3  For example, Boyd, K. M. (1979), *The Ethics of Resource Allocation in Health Care* (Edinburgh University Press), pp. 17–18.

4  For example the concept of 'indifference' in welfare economics as applied to health resource allocation. See Culyer, J. J. (1976), *Need and the National Health Service*. London, Martin Robertson.

5  For instance, Marx, K., 'Economic and philosophical manuscripts [of 1844]', *Marx Engels Collected Works* (Moscow 1975 (Progress)), iii, 277, 336; Marcuse, H. (1969), *Eros and Civilization* (London, Allen Lane), pp. 127–8; Sartre, J.-P. (1979), *Being and Nothingness* (London, Methuen), pp. 35, 83, 444, 465. Sartre uses 'existence' where 'essence' is used by other writers in the essentialist tradition, and gives 'essence' another meaning.

6  Daniels, N. (1981), 'Health care needs and distributive justice' *Philosophy and Public Affairs*, pp. 152–3; included as chapter in *Just Health Care* (1985). Cambridge University Press.

7  Here the word 'adventitious' is not used in the sense in which Daniels (ibid.) discusses 'adventitious needs'.

8  Freud, S. (1957), *Instincts and their Vicissitudes* (London, Norton), p. 123; *The Interpretation of Dreams* (1977) (Harmondsworth, Penguin), p. 715.

9  Contrast Doyal and Gough, op. cit., pp. 10, 15f.

10  Szasz denies that there is any such thing as functional mental disorder. See Szasz, T. (1971), *The Manufacture of Madness: a comparative study of the Inquisition and the Mental Health Movement* (London, Routledge & Kegan Paul), p. 124.

11  Kitson, A. (1985), 'Feeling better and getting better'. Paper at Ethical Issues in Caring 4th Conference, Manchester 1985; and in this volume.

12  Kennedy, I. (1976), 'The Karen Quinlan case: problems and proposals', *Journal of Medical Ethics*, ii, pp. 2–7.
13  Forsyth, G. (1961), *Doctors and State Medicine* (London, Pitman), p. 101.
14  Plant, op. cit. pp. 9–10.
15  McCloskey, J. H. (1976), 'Human needs, rights and political values', *American Philosophical Quarterly*, xiii, pp. 2, 9, 10.
16  The idea that the concept of justice is only relevant to certain social circumstances can be traced back at least as far as Hume. See Hume, D. A. (1972), *Treatise of Human Nature* (London, Fontana), iii, p. 218f.

# 12 Community social work and the limits of commitment

*Chris Clark*

## Introduction

In 1980 the then Secretary of State for Social Services instigated a review of the role and tasks of social workers under the auspices of the National Institute for Social Work. The resulting report (Barclay, 1982) asserted the validity and importance of what social workers do, and dealt with a wide range of issues affecting the status and development of social work both as a profession and as a local government service. The most notable aspect of its recommendations has been its adoption of community social work as the preferred model for the future of local authority social services. Although the Barclay Committee did not invent the concept of community social work, it has given the idea a moderately clear definition and identity. Also, and this is perhaps more important, Barclay legitimated community social work as an approach worthy of serious debate. Various developments in the direction of community social work, especially so-called patch working, which had been taking place more or less independently, have come to be seen, by some people at least, as parts of a broad and growing movement. Responses to the Barclay ideas have varied from enthusiastic approval for community social work on both practical and ideological grounds to scepticism as to its relevance and feasibility, and to a radical dismissal of the whole system as fundamentally misconceived and inappropriate. One of the more interesting things about the committee's work were the two minority reports, which departed in opposite directions from the ideas of the main report.

While it would be unwise to expect too rigorous a definition of an approach to practice which is still in its formative stages, the main features of community social work are soon summarised. The starting point for community social work is an observation. When we look at the ways in which caring for the vulnerable and dependent – and this means everyone at different points of their life – is organised, we soon discover that the role of the formal social services is relatively extremely small. The social care provided by social workers and other welfare professionals pales into insignificance beside the volume and quality of ordinary daily caring provided by family and friends. In our society of course it is done largely by women either as mothers or as close relatives of adult dependants. Once this fact is recognised the next stage of the argument follows fairly straightforwardly. Social workers, it says, should not even attempt to carry the major burden of social care or allow themselves to develop any illusions that they are in fact doing so. Instead of seeing themselves as having prime responsibility for actually carrying out social care, they should work in a spirit of partnership with ordinary people in the community who in fact carry most of the burdens and rewards of social caring. The third stage of the argument says that in order to do this properly it is essential to work closely with the local community and make use of the powerful and extensive systems of informal care to be found there. We can speak here of a change of focus: the worker should not merely look upon the individual client as it were in isolation but in his place within the community and his network of support and kinship and so on. For this reason the Barclay Report refers to social workers having both their traditional reponsibility for what it calls 'counselling' and a responsibility for 'social care planning'. In community social work the aim is consciously to interweave statutory and informal care in a manner which is mutually reinforcing.

Now these proposals raise a number of issues. We should ask if the underlying social analysis is correct; for example what are the realities of informal social care in our society? We must ask if community social work is a workable model in practice. On that point it should be noted that there is an interesting literature describing various local projects (for example, Hadley and McGrath, 1980; Hadley and Cooper, 1984). Many of these projects are concerned with patch working, where the emphasis is on a highly localised arrangement of social work services which, it is hoped, enables the practitioners to make intensive and systematic use of their knowledge of the local community. There are also several research projects devoted to the formal evaluation of community-oriented methods of working (especially Hadley and McGrath, 1984; Bayley *et al.*, 1985). However these are not the questions I propose to take up here. My main theme is to examine the questions of political purpose and social value which the community social work idea raises; to explore the distinctive features of community social work at the ethical and political level. I hope incidentally to show that the ethical and political issues implicit here are not essentially different from those associated with other approaches to social work or other welfare interventions. Apart from its topicality therefore the moral and political analysis of community social work might illustrate some of the things which need to be taken into account in any such analysis of social interventions.

### The politics of community social work

The concept of community social work has attracted some notoriety because of the political position, or positions, it allegedly represents. It is of great significance that the model has been both welcomed and criticised by elements from all parts of the political spectrum. Roughly the arguments go as follows. Some conservatives welcome community social work because it seems to give a relatively minor role to state-sponsored welfare services, and on the other hand it explicitly attaches high importance to the virtues of self-help. Community social work can be seen as promoting the community's own caring resources, which are seen as intrinsically preferable to anything the state could or should attempt to provide. In other words the ethic of self-reliance is bolstered and the intrusive arm of the state is kept further away from those affairs of the private citizen which should be none of the state's concern. Private charity is given scope for proper expression. Also of course community social work might enable some economies to be made in state welfare spending. Apart from the supposed economic benefits that follow, reduced taxation is a further diminution of the state's interference in the liberties of the individual. A more cynical view is that the possibility of cuts is the real reason for support of community social work from the political right.

However community social work is not solely the creature of the right. It is no accident that an early article on patch working appeared in a book entitled *Radical Social Work and Practice* (Bennett, 1980). In spite of what I have said about the conservative view the possible attractions of community social work for a socialist are not difficult to make out. The socialist might welcome community social work because of its stress on 'the community' and on 'community'. By the first I mean that community social work seems to implicate ordinary members of the community much more fully in planning and delivering social services than the traditional model with all its associations of bureaucratic inflexibility and irrelevance and town hall paternalism. For the socialist the features of community social work which stress adaptability to local conditions and the opportunity for members of the community to have a genuine role in shaping the local service are obviously attractive.

Secondly in referring to 'community' I am using a shorthand expression to denote the elements of the socialist faith which cherish community as a social value: this is also called fraternity or fellowship. Community social work is seen as a way of fostering genuine relationships of mutuality and fraternity within the neighbourhood. However despite these attractions of community social work for the political left there are also elements from the left who are profoundly suspicious of community social work. For them the references to community and participation are simply window-dressing on policies the real aim of which is to cut welfare expenditure. Such a course of action would presumably affect the poorest and weakest most severely and is therefore anti-socialist. As cuts are made the burden of replacing those contributions to social care formerly made by the state-funded social services tends to fall upon the shoulders of those who are themselves in a relatively deprived position. Private charity of course is objectionable to the left for the familiar reasons of arbitrariness leading to unequal treatment of equally needy individuals and groups, and placing the needy person in the position of supplicant rather than recipient by right.

There is a third political position, which is important because support for community social work has been most visible from its direction, and it dominates the Barclay Report. I refer here to the social democratic centre, who present a conception which offers all the comforts and ambiguities of woolly liberalism. According to this view (for example, Hadley and Hatch, 1981), the aims of the traditional socialist social welfare policies of the Beveridge era are laudable, but the instruments adopted for their implementation have proved in the event to be defective. Now it may well be true that state social services are remote, inflexible, bureaucratic and insensitive to the infinite variety of local needs and conditions. They are also therefore inefficient. Community social work would not abandon the broadly universalist conception of social work which underlies, say, the Seebohm Report; but it would aim for a more decentralised model of service delivery where variation in the service provided is legitimate in view of the variations in local and individual needs, demands and opinions. Local accountability gains precedence over uniformity of provision and centrally determined policies. There is more than an echo here of the community politics beloved of the Liberal Party. In its attempt to combine the best of everything there is obviously something attractive about the social democratic position. However, as I shall argue presently, this stand is built on ambiguity about the basis of responsibility for welfare provision and is therefore, I think, inherently unstable. This will become clearer if we first examine the basic premises informing the three political positions I have sketched.

The question of the general philosophical differences between the left and the right is a matter of some complexity. One way to approach it is to consider the different valuations the left and right each give to the values of *freedom* and *justice*. (For a fuller discussion see Clark with Asquith, 1985). The modern political right are the heirs of classical liberalism. For them the key value to be defended is freedom, and particularly that version of freedom which stresses the *absence* of man-made restraints on liberty – what Berlin (1969) calls negative freedom. So for modern conservatives community social work could be attractive because it seems to enhance individual liberty; it seeks to reduce the level of state interference in the management of social care and return to the citizen more of the initiative and responsibility for deciding whether, and how, special arrangements for securing social care are needed in any given instance. In the terms alluded to in my title it *reduces* formal state commitments and thereby possibly increases individual moral commitments. By minimising in certain ways the extent of formally organised social care the citizen (on this view) is left at greater liberty to decide whether to seek or offer special or extraordinary arrangements for procuring it.

For the left the priorities are different. Socialism is much more worried about having political arrangements which will lead to social *justice*, and socialists are prepared to accept a reduction in what they would see as the spurious freedoms of the conservatives; the famous example is their dismissal of the classical liberal version of freedom as no more than freedom to starve. There are of course many different versions of socialism and social justice which cannot be explored here. Nevertheless, to return to the context of community social work, we can safely say that for socialists the key point is that, under contemporary conditions, social services are a necessary instrument for promoting social justice. This contrasts with the conservative view of social services as something which unfortunately cannot be avoided completely but which should be reduced to the minimal level. Community social work is seen by the left as an effective means of reducing injustices in certain areas of social life. So in terms of my title community social work for socialists is a way of fulfilling more effectively the collective moral commitment to universal welfare. Community social work represents, in other words, a moral and practical commitment which is expanded both in terms of the number of people for whom a responsibility is expressed and in terms of the quality of that commitment. And that is the contrast I would like to draw with the conservative position.

Plant *et al.* (1980, ch. 4) applies a somewhat similar distinction when he argues that there are two views on the nature of the obligation to provide welfare. On the one hand the provision of welfare is seen as a matter of charity, entailing no strict duty. This view favours non-state welfare provision. On the other hand the provision of welfare is seen as a matter of strict obligation requiring legal backing.

### Whose commitment? Whose obligation?
When we talk of 'commitments' we mean in effect responsibilities; the things we have accepted a responsibility to do or the persons to whom we recognise duties. On the other hand when we talk of someone's 'com-

mitment' we refer to his or her sense of loyalty or obligation or faithfulness or devotion to a person or a cause. Now if we look at the respective attitudes of the left and right to community social work we see that, for the left, community social work implies a view of social work *commitments* (that is, responsibilities) which is *extensive*: practically everybody is seen as sharing the responsibility for formal social care. But for the right community social work puts into practice a view of social work commitments which is highly *restrictive*; only a hard core of statutory work need concern paid social workers as the rest would be done by ordinary citizens. Similarly the quality of *commitment* (that is, sense of obligation) characteristic of the left and right differs. For the left there is a sense of commitment diffused through the community and uniting all members of the community to each other. For the right moral commitments are strictly the individual's own affair.

Where does this leave the social democratic centre? Partnership, which has been stressed as a central principle in community social work, would seem to distribute the commitments. Partnership is certainly highly consonant with the centrist political position of the Barclay Report. From a practical point of view a partnership of the statutory and voluntary sectors seems eminently reasonable, sensible and realistic. However the notion of partnership is incoherent unless and until one defines rather carefully who the partners are, and which elements in the partnership are responsible for what. This is something which Barclay fails to do in a sufficiently developed way. It is, I suggest, in consequence of vagueness on this crucial point that community social work so readily appears both attractive and repellent to left and right. What is needed therefore is an elaboration of partnership as a practice concept which is not rendered worthless by concealed ambiguities. Only when this is done is it possible to make sense of community social work as political friend or foe. As it is community social work promises all things to all men because the basic issues of social value have been fudged. Here lies the instability in the centrist position to which I referred above. Community social work easily lends itself to contradictory interpretations of basic political values, and specifically to opposing conceptions of freedom and justice. Its attractiveness lies perhaps in its appearing to blunt the horns of several classic dilemmas but in fact it has not offered any real resolution of them; we still have to make up our minds which versions of freedom and justice we wish to support.

What might partnership between the social worker and the community mean in practical terms? This rather glib phrase, which the Barclay Report hardly goes beyond, conceals a number of complicated issues. We can start by asking *who* the partners are supposed to be.

Assuming for the moment that they are individual persons involved in providing social care in a given instance, we have a list including at least the following:

- the social worker
- other welfare workers both in and outside the social worker's agency
- the client
- the client's family, and others who have a presumptive duty to care for him
- the volunteer, that is, someone recruited by the agency to help provide an identified service
- the neighbour/stranger – other persons who come to know of the client's need.

One might try to go on and work out some sort of division of labour between these persons: but tackled in these simplistic terms such an attempt would be bound to fail. This is because one cannot meaningfully try to spell out, for example, the social worker's responsibilities without reference to the nature of the agency which employs him and the political mandate which supports it. Or to take another example, one cannot identify the responsibilities which lie with the client's own family without some prior social and moral theory to describe the family's responsibility. The same may be said of all the persons listed; it is impossible to spell out duties in a vacuum. In other words we must reject a conception of the problem which presents it just as a problem for individual persons treated as if they were autonomous units. What we have here is essentially a *political* problem which cannot be addressed as if the persons listed lived on the philosopher's otherwise desert island. As far as I know such places do not usually boast social services departments.

An alternative way of asking who the partners in social care are supposed to be is to list the bodies or institutions involved. These include:

- the social work agency
- other state agencies (for example health, housing, income, maintenance and so on)
- voluntary organisations
- the local state generally
- the national state
- the community.

Stated this way I think the problem becomes fairly obvious. While it was possible to be moderately sure about who the individuals were in the first list, in the second there are many ambiguities about who exactly makes up each of the collective entities, and indeed about what they are anyway. For example the social work agency is part of the local state and part of the national state; and community can mean just about anything. Here of course we encounter the key problems of political philosophy. In rejecting a narrowly individualistic social theory we must then try to work out the mutual relationship of the individual and the collective.

Having looked at the problems of deciding *who* is in the partnership we may extend this preliminary reconnaisance by asking *what* partnership should entail. Evidently a partnership is some kind of contract freely entered into by parties competent to do so. Partners accept a system of mutually binding obligations in pursuit of some joint purpose or purposes. Now even this brief statement shows up the inadequacy of the Barclay proposal. Not only is it unclear who the partners are, it is also unclear exactly what they are expected to do or what they are to expect of each other. The planning of social care is really such a nebulous objective that it would be difficult to know whether one was even aiming in the right general direction. Specifically one would have to decide where *social* care begins and ends, and be clear about its relationship to other areas of social life (such as, for instance, the economic) before one could be sure of the framework for social care planning. Welfare is not the exclusive province of social services, as Titmuss (1968) often reminded us.

The problem with the Barclay proposal is then, that its attractiveness is bought at the price of ambiguity. Inventing something called community social work can most certainly be a convenient camouflage for these basic differences of social value – differences which people sometimes like to conceal for reasons including political expediency. The characteristic vagueness of social-democratic conceptions of responsibility for the provision of welfare accounts for the justifiable unease which the Barclay ideas have aroused: they may represent a wolf in sheep's clothing. I think such suspicions are perfectly sensible and should be treated seriously.

**A remedial proposal**

Is it possible to make the Barclay concept of partnership more coherent? I shall not try to present a complete reformulation of community social work, but I would like to draw attention to one area where remedial work is urgently needed. This emerges from the second list of possible partners quoted above. In Britain social work is dominated by the local authorities who are supposed in some sense to represent the local community. Of course nobody imagines that it really works like that. The *nature* of the work that social services departments do is, arguably, primarily controlled by legislation and central government regulation, while the *volume* and *location* of the work are under some secondary control of the local authority. What is clear is that the local community has only a relatively tiny amount of influence on the nature of the local social work service. The best they are likely to have is one councillor on the social services committee, and even he can easily disregard the local views about social work. If we are ever to have *community* social work, therefore, we need a much more robust identity for the local community. By this I mean first that the theoretical and political nettle of what exactly we mean by the phrase 'local community' will have to be firmly grasped. Secondly there would need to be some proper constitutional machinery for giving the local community a major say in the running of their social work service. In practice this would have to mean that some degree of control of spending powers – and perhaps even revenue powers as well – lay within the local community. This is a far cry from the purely consultative role of existing community and parish councils. Such a shifting of financial powers down to the level of populations of 5000 or so would truly be a radical departure from the British tradition of government. It would mean a major shift towards some kind of local socialism. The only comparable model I can think of is the system of organisation of social care at the level of the commune which has been developed in China and one or two other places (Dixon, 1981, 1982). If this is what the Barclay Committee foresaw, it is hardly surprising they were coy about it.

Such a radical departure does not seem likely in the immediate future. However it is possible to envisage more cautious reforms that might at least act as pathfinders for change. Social work teams who wished to practise community social work could set up some sort of local community council which would have the job of promoting better 'social care planning'. This body might well be distinct from existing community councils and the like. If this proposal is not to result in mere tokenism, social workers and their managers would have to be prepared to allow the nature of their work to be controlled at least in part by the decisions of the local community assembly. Inevitably concepts of professional responsibility would have to be substantially revised.

I do not wish to imply that setting up such an assembly would be straightforward. It is easy to imagine situations that most social work managers, and local politicians, would find nightmarish. Commenting on the decentralisation of local authority functions in Islington, Price (1985, p. 24) notes that 'one fear must be for a majority party to lose its control of a particular neighbourhood committee to a concentration of other interests, be they elected or non elected'. Suppose that the local community proved to have racist views. What would happen if they wished to implement a pattern of services which the social workers thought was unfair, inefficient or just impractical? How would social workers with their welfare ideology cope with a retributivist community attitude to deviance? In spite of these very real and serious problems there is certainly evidence that the issue of local accountability has been recognised by instigators of community social work projects. The Barclay Committee itself proposed that there should be 'local welfare advisory committees' which would be 'designed to provide a forum in which representatives of clients, employers and social workers could discuss agency policies with respect to the rights of clients' (1982, pp. 192–3).

Cooper (1980, pp. 39–40) writes of a 'Social Care Assembly for Normanton', an open forum or 'local "united nations"'; elsewhere it is described as 'a way in which the responsibility of the town for its own people can be fully developed and the care of voluntary and statutory agencies fully coordinated' (Hadley and McGrath, 1984, p. 183). SCAN received funding from the Home Office Voluntary Service Unit (Cooper, 1983, p. 161). The research team on the Normanton project reports that the following themes dominated the meetings in the early days: accommodation for groups; the need for information about groups; possibilities of community care; facilities for youth; organisation of SCAN itself (Hadley and McGrath, 1984, p. 183). The key point in this context however is that SCAN was envisaged as a purely consultative body, without executive power over the management of the local statutory service. It therefore falls a long way short of the full partnership referred to above.

The instigators and researchers of the Dinnington project fully recognise the problem of community representation, and observe that the project substantially failed to achieve it:

> Once the Project was under way efforts were made to remedy [the lack of real involvement in the community] by the inclusion of seven community representatives on the Project Management Team. However, they found it very difficult to take a constructive part in proceedings. They felt that the meetings were dominated by the professionals... The Project has shown how difficult it is to build in genuine participation by local people, if it is not built in at a very early stage, however good the intentions. (Bayley *et al.*, 1985, p. 117)

The wider issues are trenchantly put forward:

> There is a profound challenge here both to politicians and managers about how far they are prepared to go in giving local people a real say in how local services are planned, managed and delivered. The Dinnington Project cannot claim to have been at all successful in this respect. (ibid. p. 118)

The debate about local representation has indeed reappeared constantly in discussion of the management of local social services. The community development strategies espoused by various local authorities at different times over the last fifteen years are testimony to that concern. A commitment to local control both substantial and lasting has however proved to be elusive: and a major reason for this must certainly be a political tradition which deeply mistrusts the competence of local people to manage local affairs except within a narrow, and centrally defined, framework.

## Community social work and socialism

The foregoing analysis leads me to the conclusion that community social work is indeed perfectly compatible with a thoroughly socialist position. Moreover it is potentially a lot more socialist than the Barclay Committee imagined. Nevertheless there are drawbacks to community social work even for a socialist, or at any rate a moderate socialist. Community social workers who worked in the kind of locally governed system I have suggested would, by definition, be under the control of some local governing assembly. The corollary of this is that they would carry the authority of that assembly to enforce upon individuals courses of action which those persons might find repugnant. If the community social workers were to be given a strong mandate for the welfare of practically everybody, we might well be worried about the threat to privacy involved. The whole problem of accountability would take on an entirely new aspect. For example, would the social worker be held accountable to the local community if he failed to contain a client's deviant behaviour? It is impossible not to feel some sympathy with the liberal who would insist upon the individual's right to refuse help in many instances. Richard Titmuss as long ago as 1965 (1968, p. 85) ascribed the following question to local government councillors and officials: 'Is there not in the claims sometimes made by social workers a fundamental threat to notions of local democracy?'

The point at issue here seems to be about what variety of socialism, if any, one would wish to adopt. The strong version of community social work which I have indicated apparently entails too high a price in terms of individual liberty, including freedom from paternalistic inter-vention, for the average social democrat; and I think it is a fairly safe guess that academic and practical workers in the field of welfare are concentrated in the social democratic part of the political spectrum. Robert Pinker brings out the underlying issue in his minority report of the Barclay Committee. Most moderate socialists, including Titmuss for example, accept that even where there exist well-supported universalist social services some selective services are still necessary to provide for the unusual need and special case. Pinker's critique is valuable for being quite clear that social work should be a selective service and not a universal one. It should have a restricted and not an inclusive mandate. On that ground, among others, he rejects community social work in favour of a slightly more professionalised version of the kind of social work we already have.

## An underlying ambiguity

I have argued that the basic premises about social need and community life which are implicit in the concept of community social work tend towards a form of service delivery and practical accountability which has all the hallmarks of a highly socialist ideology. Beginning with the Barclay idea about social care one is led to a strongly socialist way of providing for it. But this realisation does not undo the interesting paradox at the heart of the Barclay approach, for the ideological sympathies of the Barclay Committee are plainly social democratic of a fairly cautious colour. In effect the logic of their argument tends to lead them in a direction they really would not want to go. This is perhaps one reason why the portrayal in the main report of what community social work would look like in practice is very much thinner and less convincing than the discussion leading up to it.

Where does this leave the right-wing view? It is less than plausible that community social work can really appeal to the conservative who stops to examine the basic assumptions behind it: as has already been argued, these assumptions would tend to lead to a socialist form of service. A properly devised community social work would increase the state's commitment to welfare, not decrease it. But of course the trappings of community social work might well be borrowed by conservatives for reasons of political expediency. It has been suggested that the proponents of community social work are naively creating legitimations for anti-welfare policies; community social work could be used to subvert welfare. I think it is also true that the conservative tradition in Britain is less worried about philosophical incompatibilities in the clutch of policies adopted at any given moment than is the socialist tradition. Conservatives have never been worried about a philosophically untidy pragmatism, whereas it is well known that socialists will argue interminably about the correct ideology.

Too much should not be expected from community social work, as the Barclay Committee might have said. The ambiguity at the heart of community social work has analogues in virtually all models of social work. This discussion may incidentally serve to heighten awareness that even mainstream social work has no clear account to offer of itself in terms of the political position and political values it represents. I am convinced that social work is a profoundly political activity, but its political personality seems to be unformed. Social work has at least the rudiments of a generally accepted ethical system which we can conveniently summarise in the phrase 'respect for persons'. There does not seem to be any comparable maxim which refers to the political character of social work. In fact where social work's political personality ought to be, there is confusion. This confusion must be cleared up before we can approve the agenda for community social work, or any other brand of social work.

## Note

An earlier version of this paper was given at the Ethical Issues in Caring conference, Manchester, September 1984. I would like to express my thanks to Stewart Asquith, Bill Bennett and Bob Brecher for their comments.

## References

Barclay, P. M. (Chairman) (1982). See National Institute for Social Work.

Bayley, M. *et al.* (1985), *Neighbourhood Services Project: Dinnington,* Paper no. 12, *The Final Report.* University of Sheffield.

Bennett, B. (1980), 'The sub-office: a team approach to local authority fieldwork practice' in Brake, M. and Bailey, R. (1980), *Radical Social Work and Practice.* Arnold.

Berlin, I. (1969), 'Two concepts of freedom' in *Four Essays on Liberty.* Oxford University Press.

Clark, C. L. with Asquith, S. (1985), *Social Work and Social Philosophy: a guide for practice.* London, Routledge & Kegan Paul.

Cooper, M. (1980), 'Normanton: interweaving social work and the community' in Hadley and McGrath (1980).

Cooper, M. (1983), 'Community social work' in Jordan, B. and Parton, N. (1983), *The Political Dimensions of Social Work.* Oxford, Blackwell.

Dixon, J. (1981), 'Community-based welfare support in China: 1949-1979', *Community Development Journal,* 16 (1).

Dixon, J. (1982), 'The community-based rural welfare system in the People's Republic of China, 1949-1979', *Community Development Journal,* 17 (1).

Hadley, R. and Cooper, M., eds (1984), *Patch based social services,* Bulletin no. 3. University of Lancaster.

Hadley, R. and Hatch, S. (1981), *Social Welfare and the Failure of the State.* London, Allen and Unwin.

Hadley, R. and McGrath, M., eds (1980), *Going local,* London, Bedford Square Press.

Hadley, R. and McGrath, M., eds (1984), *When Social Services are Local: the Normanton experience.* London, Allen and Unwin.

National Institute for Social Work (1982), *Social Workers: their role and tasks* (Chairman P. M. Barclay). London, Bedford Square Press.

Plant, R., Lesser, H. and Taylor-Gooby, P. (1980), *Political Philosophy and Social Welfare.* London, Routledge & Kegan Paul.

Price, J. R. (1985), 'Decentralisation in Islington' in Hatch, S., ed, *Decentralisation and Care in the Community.* Policy Studies Institute.

*Report of the Committee on Local Authority and Allied Personal Social Services* (1968) (Chairman F. Seebohm). Cmnd. 3703.

Titmuss, R. M. (1968), 'Social work and social service: a challenge for local government' in *Commitment to Welfare.* London, Allen and Unwin.

# 13 Quality of life and services for people with disabilities

*Peter Mittler*

The year 1981 was designated by the United Nations as the International Year of Disabled Persons. The key words for the year were *equality* and *participation*. I would like to examine some of the implications of these words and to invite you to contrast the rhetoric with the reality. I shall not attempt to define quality of life but I will argue that one important constituent concerns the opportunity to make choices between perceived alternatives. I shall apply this criterion to people with disabilities and ask you to consider the extent to which they are provided with opportunities to make choices about the way in which they live, and how their range of choices compares with those available to others.

The concept of choice on the basis of perceived and understood alternatives can also be applied to professionals who make decisions and give advice to people with disabilities and their families. It applies with particular force to those of our fellow citizens whom we elect or apppoint to positions of influence and who, as local authority councillors or members of health authorities, are entrusted with key decisions about priorities and the allocation of ever-dwindling resources. The choices they make are not necessarily matters of life and death but they are part of a continuum of decision-making affecting the quality of life available not only to disabled people but to all of us.

## The right to treatment

Two events which made a major impact on the public during 1982 were concerned with an open debate about whether infants with severe handicapping conditions should be allowed to live. The first involved a baby with Down's syndrome who was born in a London teaching hospital and diagnosed as having an intestinal obstruction which could be corrected by a routine surgical procedure. The parents refused to give their consent to the operation, thus consigning the baby to certain death within days. The local Director of Social Services promptly took legal action to make the child a ward of court and used his powers to give consent to the operation. The child is alive and well and is now in the care of foster parents.

The second case involved the trial of a paediatrician who was alleged to have been responsible for the death of another infant with Down's syndrome. He was found not guilty of manslaughter and discharged.

The case of a third child with Down's syndrome was much discussed in the United States. This concerns a twelve-year-old boy whose parents had consigned him to an institution at birth and had subsequently not maintained further contact with him except for a very few visits and cards. At the age of twelve it was discovered that the boy had a major heart defect which required urgent surgery. The parents refused to give consent to the operation and also tried to use the courts to prevent further contact between the boy and a family that had befriended him and regularly invited him into their home.

These cases were widely discussed in the press and in professional journals and gave rise to what was on the whole a very serious and high-level debate. Certainly the issues are exceedingly complex and raise many fundamental questions concerning the rights of parents to make decisions and to have the last word in determining whether their child should live or die, and on the role of professionals in advising parents and in helping them to make a painful and agonising decision. The debate also reflected a very wide range of opinion on the right to life, from those who argued that there are no circumstances in which it is justifiable to allow a child to die when its life might be saved by medical intervention, to those who took the view that parents have a total right to decide that the child should be allowed to die and that it is the duty of doctors to abide by the wishes of the parents in this matter.

For at least ten years there had been a good deal of discussion within the health professions, some of it public and some distinctly acrimonious, concerning the use of surgical and medical intervention in the case of babies with neural tube defects such as spina bifida. Some doctors claimed to be able to give a prognosis concerning the future quality of life of a handicapped child on the basis of specific clinical characteristics such as the site of the lesion. Decisions would be made on the basis of such prognoses whether to operate on the child or to allow the child to die.

The ethical and professional issues which are posed by these cases are extremely delicate and complex and should not be simplified or polarised. I certainly do not feel able to argue that there are no circumstances in which doctors should not do everything possible to maintain life, no matter how irreparably damaged a child may be, or to struggle to keep alive a baby that cannot in any case live for more than a short time. I feel more confident where children with Down's syndrome are concerned because I know that very many of them do lead enjoyable and full lives, that they can be helped to learn by skilled teaching and habilitation and that many can live and work with support in the community. Some of the statements made by specialists concerning prospects for people with Down's syndrome are simply not based on a knowledge of the facts as we know them but on what was written in the textbooks a generation ago.

*Predicting quality of life?*

I do not therefore wish to comment further on these cases themselves. Instead I would like to examine some of the wider issues concerning common assumptions about disabled and handicapped people, and to look at some cherished beliefs about the goals of services which we provide in an effort to meet their needs.

The first point I would like to single out concerns the assumption that some people are so severely handicapped that their lives cannot be worth living and that they are better off dead. It has been seriously maintained that it would be actually in the child's best interests to be allowed to die. Whether such a statement can morally or logically be made by one human being about another can be debated on philosophical grounds. My concern here is with the nature of the *professional* judgment involved. How far can a doctor make predictions about the future personal and social development of a baby with a handicapping condition? To what extent is the doctor making clinical judgments based on sound inference and to what extent are they affected by value judgments concerning quality of life? For example the doctor may conclude on the basis of a clinical examination that the nature and site of the lesions in a baby born with spina bifida are such that the child will never be able to walk independently or will never be able to control bladder and bowel functions. This knowledge, assuming that it is accurate, certainly has implications for the quality of life that will be led by that individual. But how do we make such judgments? Disabilities which seem intolerable to one person may seem less so to others; how can we reconcile the vastly different perceptions of the paediatrician, the parents and those of the affected person (who is not consulted at all at this stage but whose interests are said to be represented by others)?

Walking and continence are relatively straightforward examples but how much more complex are judgments about intelligence? This raises issues about the value which our society places on intelligence and achievement, characteristics which are highly developed in those who have to make the crucial decision. Some of the literature on spina bifida suggests that an IQ under 80 should be regarded as one of the criteria for non-intervention despite the fact that this level of intellectual functioning comprises some 10 per cent of the general population. If inability to walk, to achieve continence or an IQ under 80 are to be regarded as indications of such poor quality of life that a handicapped infant is better off dead, then what implications does this have for people who acquire these disabilities in later life as a result of accident, illness or just old age? Is it morally different to take steps to stop a life that has just begun than to terminate the life of a person who becomes incapacitated? Are judgments about impaired quality of life different when a person loses capacities once possessed than when a newborn baby is on the threshold of a life marked by impairment, disability and handicap?

We can note the even more challenging dilemma posed by the unborn child who is known to be impaired. It is thought to be reasonable to do everything possible to prevent the birth of a baby with spina bifida or Down's syndrome; for this reason we carry out tests early in a pregnancy on women at risk and recommend abortion of a foetus that is proved to be abnormal. But the majority of handicapped infants cannot be diagnosed prenatally; once they are born it is generally assumed that everything must be done to maintain life. The significance of recent events is that some of these assumptions have been explicitly challenged.

## Quality of services

For those that do survive we need to look critically at the quality of services which our society provides for people with disabilities, especially for those with intellectual disabilities, and consider the extent to which these services can be said to enhance quality of life for those they purport to serve. If these services are so deficient that they impair rather than enhance quality of life, how far does our society take this into account in insisting that handicapped infants have a right to life? What quality of life are we talking about? Is it one we would wish for ourselves? In fact anyone familiar with our services for disabled people will find a very uneven pattern. Many handicapped people still live in very poor conditions with low levels of staffing and very little treatment or training. Many others, particularly the younger generation, are benefiting from well-planned and well-staffed services which respect the dignity of the individual. Nearly all are close to or well below the official poverty line.

### Universal rights

It seems relevant to examine these developments in relation to general declarations concerning the rights of all human beings, which have been promulgated by the United Nations and which are in some cases protected through the courts; in addition more specific international declarations have also been made concerning the rights of children, of disabled people in general and of mentally handicapped people in particular. Needless to say these statements are couched in the most general terms and some are qualified almost out of recognition by phrases such as 'wherever possible', 'to the maximum extent possible' and, in recent UK legislation, 'subject to the availability of resources'.

Nevertheless recent experience has shown that these declarations, while having all the hallmarks of rhetoric, can be used as the basis of positive discrimination or, as the Americans put it, affirmative action. In the United States skilful use has been made of the courts to implement civil rights for minority groups and to ensure access both to general services used by all citizens and to specialised services arising from specific needs. In this country parent groups have come very close to using the courts to declare government ministers or local authorities in dereliction of their duty – for example in failing to provide full-time education up to the age of nineteen years for mentally handicapped students – but somehow ministers or local government directors nearly always seem to avoid court action by appearing to concede the point at issue, only to backtrack at a later stage. In Oxfordshire, for example, it was agreed, following pressure from the DES and the initiation of legal proceedings by parents and others, that education would be extended beyond sixteen. When legal proceedings had been withdrawn it became apparent that education would only be provided for 'those likely to benefit' and then only on a part-time basis. Young people who had been thought to be capable of benefiting from full-time education till the age of sixteen were suddenly judged to be incapable of benefiting when they reached their sixteenth birthday.

*Self-advocacy and the chance to choose*
With or without the courts there are signs that disabled people are beginning to insist on their rights and are becoming increasingly articulate about the quality of services being provided for them. In particular they are demanding the right to participate in decision-making concerning their own future as individuals; disabled people are also asking to be formally represented on official committees planning future services, at both local and national level. There are several increasingly powerful associations of disabled people; these are by no means confined merely to the most able or to the most articulate.

Many professionals in this country are surprised to learn about the North American People First movement which is entirely run by mentally handicapped people helped by one or two advisers; like other associations they have regional and national conferences, elect officers, run meetings to discuss issues of importance to their membership, make representations to local and national government and use the media. Even in this country about a quarter of the Adult Training Centres –

which in total cater for more people than the population of our mental handicap hospitals – have student committees. One of these won the right for members of all these centres to join the National Union of Students (Williams and Shoultz, 1982; Crawley, 1983).

The growing self-advocacy movement is a new phenomenon that will need to be taken into account in discussing issues concerned with the quality of life and the right to life. I recently attended an international session of the People First organisation in Canada which was discussing compulsory sterilisation of mentally handicapped people – still commonly practised in parts of North America. It was felt that mentally handicapped people had the same right as anyone else to have children but that many needed help in looking after children and that it was up to parents and professionals to ensure that they should exercise choice in this matter. In fact there is evidence that mentally handicapped people who do marry or who have stable relationships with a partner are usually very careful to ensure that they do not have children and recognise that they may have difficulty in fulfilling their responsibilities as parents.

Handicapped people then, are demanding a much greater degree of participation in decision-making concerning their own lives and the lives of other disabled people. But decision-making involves learning how to make choices between meaningfully presented alternatives and many handicapped people lack not only the experiences but also the opportunities to learn to make the simplest choices. The choice of what to wear or what to eat is rarely available because it is easier or quicker for others to make these decisions for them, even though there is evidence to indicate that even people with very severe intellectual impairments are able to show clear preferences when presented with two alternatives. This should not be surprising, since babies only a few weeks old can also express choice in what they look at or listen to, if given the means of expressing that choice.

If the ability to make choices between perceived alternatives is one way of judging quality of life, we have to accept that many handicapped people lack opportunities to express choice not only in clothes and food but also in their choice of where they are to live, the kind of schools they go to, the kinds of work that they would like to do, the way they spend their leisure. They are often restricted in their social and sexual relationships and making a home and having children.

These impediments to a reasonable quality of life apply to many disabled people who are living and working in the community, but they are very much more in evidence for the majority of people who are living in long-stay hospitals. Hundreds of thousands of people in hospitals for the mentally ill, the mentally handicapped, the elderly, and the chronic sick and disabled, experience very little choice in their everyday living. Although there have certainly been major improvements in the physical amenities of such hospitals, shortage of staff and the dead weight of institutional routine soon lead to boredom, apathy, loss of initiative and institutional neurosis, as richly described in the novel *One Flew over the Cuckoo's Nest* as in any of the classical research studies.

If people who make decisions about priorities and the allocations of scarce resources - ministers, MPs, elected local councillors and appointed officers - were to spend even one night a year as patients in a long-stay hospital they might ask themselves whether they would care to live the rest of their lives in such a setting.

## Goals and dilemmas

The reality of day-to-day living for many disabled people is well documented but the rhetoric continues. So I want briefly to examine the logic of the rhetoric and to ask how far we are justified in maintaining it with slogans and speeches, with White Papers and Acts of Parliament and in what we teach our students.

Rhetoric serves an important purpose. It helps us to set goals and gives us principles to guide not only our path to the future but also our day-to-day practice. Rhetoric is not harmful in itself; few are deceived by it and even fewer mistake rhetoric for reality. But rhetoric does induce complacency. It makes us feel that we are on the way to achieving our admirable and worthy-sounding goals and to forget how far we still are from achieving them. Perhaps this is why media exposés of conditions in our long-stay hospitals make such a major impact. The public are shocked into a reminder that people living in some long-stay hospitals are still sleeping thirty or more to a room, that many of them spend most of their days without anything to do, without training or rehabilitation or occupation, and that two members of staff may be supervising thirty residents. There follows the inevitable public inquiry, possibly some staff are dismissed or even put on trial, attempts are made to institute improved management procedures, maybe a little guilt money becomes available, and the whole cycle recommences.

What then, are some of the essential constituents of the rhetoric and what implications do they have for our discussion on quality of life? A fundamental assumption of the philosophy underpinning planning is that disabled people are full and equal citizens with the same rights and responsibilities as all other citizens. This means that they should have full and equal access to all the resources and services used by everyone else - education, health, social, housing and employment services, attending ordinary schools, receiving primary medical care and whatever specialist services they need, living in ordinary houses either with their families or independently with staff support, working or being trained to work according to their need. They clearly need the financial means to be economically independent and to enjoy access to leisure activities of their choosing.

These principles were first set out in relation to mental handicap in a government White Paper in 1971 and have been frequently reaffirmed. For example, the Jay Committee of Enquiry into Nursing and Care (1979) developed three principles which have been accepted by the government and by the relevant professional and parent associations.

(i)   Mentally handicapped people have the right to enjoy normal patterns of life within the community.

(ii)  Mentally handicapped people have the right to be treated as individuals.

(iii) Mentally handicapped people will require additional help from the communities in which they live and from professional service if they are to develop their maximum potential as individuals.

I have deliberately contrasted these fine principles with the reality of life and conditions in long-stay hospitals. This is not to discredit the principles as idealistic and incapable of realisation but to underline the problems involved in moving away from service patterns that we have inherited from the past and which are now regarded as anachronistic - beliefs in segregation, generally many miles from centres of population buttressed by an underlying concern for the protection of the public from deviant minorities who might threaten the stability and sense of well-being of society, the need to prevent reproduction of the unfit by isolation and sometimes sterilisation.

How do we move from where we are to where we want to be? Some countries such as Italy are trying to adopt an approach that is literally radical – they have closed their institutions and special schools by Act of Parliament and simply uprooted their inhabitants into the community. The Italians argue that they would never do this if they waited till they were ready for integration – till the public was ready to accept handicapped and mentally ill people as fellow citizens – till they had the resources to staff community services and provide support for existing staff. They do not claim that these measures will benefit all the people that have been uprooted. But they do believe that they are laying foundations for the fuller acceptance and integration of the next generation of handicapped people by preparing the public – and particularly schoolchildren – to receive them as fellow citizens.

In this country we adopt a more pragmatic incremental approach. We have concentrated on preventing admission to our hospitals by building up better community services – better schools, better support systems for families, more financial assistance, improved health care. This approach has worked well for children; hardly any children are now admitted for long-term care to mental handicap hospitals and the majority of children in the hospitals have become adults. By the end of the 1980s there should be virtually no children left in hospitals.

But there are still 45 000 adults living in hospitals for the mentally handicapped, a substantial number of whom do not need to be there. The same applies to a much larger number of people in hospitals for the mentally ill. And many thousands of adults are still admitted to hospitals because we do not have the community services to meet their needs.

Here we arrive at a paradox. The ideology of community services is accepted by most people, including many of those who work in the hospitals. And yet we pour large sums of money into the hospitals – because they are there, because the buildings need to be maintained, because the people in them deserve a better quality of life, because we know that most of those who are there now will spend the rest of their lives there, because the public wants them there and often opposes a proposal to put a house for handicapped people in their street, because we do not have the money to develop community services for all who need them.

This brings us to a second dilemma. The principle that handicapped people should have full access to ordinary community services has run up against the reality that it is precisely these ordinary community services which are being eroded and undermined by cuts in public expenditure. Local government and social services in particular are taking the brunt of expenditure cuts and yet these are the very services that are being asked to assume a much greater share of the responsibility for meeting the needs of handicapped people. A former minister for the disabled in the present government repeatedly stated that if the disabled really want to be seen as citizens in the mainstream of society they must face the harsh economic realities confronting the country and accept their share of the hardship along with their fellow citizens. No question here of positive discrimination, no allowance for the low base rate from which they were starting, little recognition of the principle of special need.

There is no easy way out of this dilemma, even if money should ever again become available. We did not solve these problems at times of growth and we are not likely to do so now without finding a new formula. Attempts are being made to solve some of the administrative and organisational obstacles which prevent resources being shifted from the National Health Service to local government; two years ago the government produced what seemed to be an innovative and exciting set of concrete proposals to transfer funds. A year of consultation, further expenditure cuts and a new ministerial team have yielded a response which, while better than nothing, is pathetically inadequate compared to the original initiative. The elephant has again given birth to a mouse

Faced with these continuing disappointments staff working in the
service, not to mention disabled people themselves, are not surprisingly
disillusioned and prone to apathy. The term 'professional depression'
has been used to describe a feeling that decision-making is out of one's
hands, that there is nothing that can be done to improve matters, a sense
of hopelessness and worthlessness at decisions that are made by others.

## The lay decision-makers

Many of the crucial decisions which affect the quality of care and service
are not made directly by traditional members of the caring professions
at all. At local government level decisions are made by elected members
of local authorities – the councillors who serve on social service,
education, housing and finance committees – who are faced with
providing a service for the whole community with zero and less than
zero growth rates. For them the disabled are only one of many
competing priorities and pressure groups. However much they want to
improve community services they can now only do so at the expense of
other services. Similar problems face the appointed members of District
Health Authorities, which were created with the explicit aim of
delegating decision-making down to smaller population units.

If critical decisions about priorities and the allocation of ever scarcer
resources are largely to be taken by democratically elected and
appointed fellow citizens, by what means and processes do they make
these decisions? If, as argued, making choices on the basis of clearly
perceived alternatives is a reflection of a high degree of responsibility,
how do they perceive the alternatives? What information is available to
help them to choose? Who advises them and what is the advice given?

I suggest that it is the lay decision-makers, the elected members of
local government and appointed members of District Health Authorities, who are in effect having to make decisions which are no less
important than those made by doctors considering whether to allow a
handicapped baby to live or die. Doctors make judgments about the
patients in front of them; they have their clinical experience and the
knowledge of their predecessors and peers to guide them in making a
prognosis and a judgment. What information and experience are
available to guide our elected representatives in making their decisions
not to go ahead with staffing a hostel that has been built, to reduce the
staffing of community services and to withdraw social work support
from families? How can they decide between repairing the boiler system
of a large hospital and the purchase of small houses for people who
might leave hospital?

*Expressing accountability*

Such decisions are made every day by committees democratically elected for the purpose. They are perhaps less dramatic than the life and death decisions which attract the attention of the media and the courts but they are far more pervasive and influential in the long run. They are also open to public scrutiny; our elected members are accountable not merely in the sense that they have to resubmit themselves for election but also to the extent that the policies and the interpretation of the policies can be called into question at any time by families, by pressure groups, by organisations for the disabled and by disabled people themselves. Compared to North America where the principle of access to records has been won through the courts, our own steps towards open local government seem halting; even so the decision-makers are still accountable.

But how often are our elected representatives or our appointed public servants called to account for their decisions? The main occasions on which this happens are when there is a crisis or a scandal or when a vigilant local group such as a Community Health Council draws attention to a chronically underfinanced sector of the service which is delivering an unacceptably low level of care and treatment. In general the public is prepared to let its elected representatives get on with the job, at least until they provide positive proof of incompetence. In effect the public has institutionalised and isolated its own elected members. They would rather not know about staffing levels in geriatric, mental illness and mental handicap hospitals, about the physical condition and the social isolation of the wards, the lack of activity for residents, nor about the many thousands of people who in the opinion of the staff itself should not be in hospital at all but living as their fellow citizens in the local community.

Elected members are not to be blamed for this situation. They are locked into a system which exalts local decision-making on local issues by locally elected people. Central government lays down policies with a very broad brush and claims not to interfere with local decisions while depriving local authorities of the resources to do anything but maintain a bare minimum of services for the ordinary public, far less for minority groups. True, a Secretary of State can declare a local authority in default of its statutory obligations but how often have these powers been used? Indeed it is local authorities who have more frequently been able to declare ministers in default of their duties. Ministers frequently say with one breath that services for disabled people should have the highest priority; with the next breath they say that of course it is for local authorities to decide their own priorities. The most recent government statement on transferring resources from health to local authorities said 'there would be no central diktat'. In other words health authorities would not be obliged to use NHS funds to discharge people from hospital, and even if they wished to do so, local authorities would not need to accept funds for this purpose.

### Quality of information
If democracy in action is local decisions made by local people, then we cannot complain if the decisions are against the interests of a particular group. What we can do is to insist that those whom we elect to make decisions are fully accountable, and that they have access to whatever information is available. Since we rely on paid officials to help them to do this, we need to ask how well informed they are on questions concerned with disability, how easily they can gain access to information and advice. The civil service at its best has highly developed skills in briefing ministers. They list alternative courses of action and indicate what in their judgment the consequences of each alternative might be. Of course they may be wrong and they may deliberately ease ministers into opting for their own preferred alternative, as we have seen in *Yes Minister* and its Radio 3 mandarin counterpart, *No Minister*. But do local government decision-makers command the skills of officials who are at least as well-read in their subject as university teachers and who are in addition rather more skilled in understanding the consequences of decisions that may be made on the basis of their briefing? Apart from tight control of expenditure the role of central government in monitoring, evaluation and control of the quality of services is limited. If they do exert an influence it is benign, unofficial and behind the scenes, or mediated through semi-independent and grossly overworked bodies such as Her Majesty's Inspectorate.

If this is so the main hope for better monitoring of the quality as well as the quantity of a service has to be sought at local level and also perhaps through informed pressure from voluntary organisations. Although in the last analysis local authorities must be accountable for their own decisions (or lack of them), there is considerable scope for the development of detailed guidelines. There are examples of guidance documents from national and professional as well as local bodies, which take the rhetoric and the philosophical goals of a service as a starting point and build on these foundations to identify specific components of the kind of service that would result from the implementation of these necessarily general service goals. For example, everyone is agreed that a much greater degree of coordination is essential to the planning and development of a comprehensive service for mentally handicapped people and that it is important to work for collaboration between health, education, social services, housing, employment and leisure services and between all of these and the voluntary sector. Since everyone claims to believe in coordination across administrative boundaries, why is it so difficult to achieve?

The kind of guidance document I have in mind can identify specific and detailed questions concerning membership of local planning groups – for example the range of membership (are consumers represented, the terms of reference, what is the chain of reporting upwards, sideways and downwards?). It can also attempt to summarise and synthesise the available information on good practice while leaving local decision-makers free, like all good scholars, to check their primary sources either by reading or by going to see whatever examples of effective services they can still find intact.

Such instruments can also be used as a means of expressing accountability. Not only are specific short-term objectives increasingly used as an integral part of planning for the individual client as well as for the professional, as in the 'nursing process', but they are also being much more skilfully used in the planning of services. The essence of the approach involves the identification of short-term objectives, defined in sufficiently clear language to enable an independent judgment to be made on whether or not the objective has been attained. There must be a clear specification not only of the objective but also of the steps to be taken to reach the goal, the criteria to be used in assessing whether the objective has been attained and an allocation of clear tasks to named individuals.

Needless to say not all service objectives lend themselves to this approach and many goals will rightly remain elusive. Not even behaviourists claim to be able to measure quality of life but at least some elements can be defined with reasonable precision. Moreover some of the instruments developed for this purpose derive clearly – some would say too rigidly – from the principle of normalisation. Stripped of jargon the principle of normalisation refers to helping handicapped people to live as normal a life-style as possible. In practice this will include involving them in ordinary community activities and avoiding practices which could be physically or socially isolating.

An instrument known as the Program Analysis of Service Systems – or PASS – has been developed in North America to assess the extent to which a particular service facility is run in accordance with principles of normalisation. In this country the National Development Group for the Mentally Handicapped (1980) developed a checklist of standards to enable staff at local level to evaluate the quality of their own services and also to provide a tool against which to assess new services still at the planning stage. Both these and similar instruments include questions concerned, *inter alia*, with the proximity of a service to other community services such as shops and public transport, whether the service blends with local surroundings and whether any elements of the service could single out clients from ordinary members of the public –

for example by the style of labelling of the building, the dress of its staff or clients, and so on (Wolfensberger and Glenn, 1975; NDG, 1980).

Evidence that such guidelines are necessary can be found in many recent local plans which manifestly do not conform to the principles of normalisation. Local and health authorities are still planning services for handicapped people on the edge of cities or far away from community services, use is made of derelict property abandoned by others – for example disused residential schools or Borstals; above all, planning is still based on the principle of congregating large numbers of people on one site, despite evidence which indicates that the majority of mentally handicapped people can learn to live in ordinary domestic-style houses with support and do not need to be herded into 96-bedded hospitals, even when these are broken down into units of 24 and 8.

I said earlier that elected members of local bodies were not to be blamed if they were not aware of all the options but that some means had to be found of exposing them to the range of choices open to them. Since they are responsible for developing services to the whole community they cannot be experts in the needs of any one group of local citizens, however special their needs. The problem is one of conveying a sense of what is possible and of combating their understandable preconception and prejudices concerning the needs of handicapped people. These might include a feeling, perhaps fostered by some local professionals, that mentally handicapped people 'are better off with their own kind', that people in institutions are apt to be violent or promiscuous or both or that the value of property will decline if handicapped people move into a neighbourhood.

*Access to all local services*
Even more important than the planning of services specifically for handicapped people is the positive and planned access of handicapped people to the ordinary services used by the rest of the community. While it is true that these are being undermined by expenditure cuts, this is no reason for creating second-class citizens who can only have access to services when times are better. Employment services provide a useful example; it is sometimes argued that it is not justifiable to train mentally handicapped people for work or to spend resources on trying to find them jobs when well over three million non-handicapped people are unemployed. More subtle variations of this theme can be heard when mentally handicapped people are denied access to services on the grounds that 'they will not appreciate them'. Some mentally handi-capped people still find it difficult to get access to wheelchairs, mobility and hearing aids, walking aids, glasses and other prosthetic devices, as well as to the services of physiotherapists and speech therapists on the grounds that 'they are unlikely to be able to benefit'.

This brings us back finally to the new-born baby. Just because a baby has a handicapping condition, is this a reason for withholding treatment procedures which would be used without question if the child were not handicapped? Operations for intestinal obstruction or cardiac anomalies are a case in point, but what about social measures? If parents of a non-handicapped child become unable for any reason to look after their child we have procedures for finding substitute families or for taking children into care. Similarly, if a single parent without family or means of support were to die in childbirth, Social Services Departments are ready at very short notice to try to find a substitute home. Why then, if the parents of a new-born handicapped child refuse to take the child home, do we hesitate to do likewise? Why, if the baby requires urgent life-saving medical or surgical treatment, do we wonder if the baby would not be better dead? Why, if a mother is so severely depressed after childbirth that she refuses to feed the baby and asks that it be left to die, do we not respect her wishes? Yet it is argued that parents who are understandably in a state of shock and grief on learning that their baby has a handicapping condition should have their wishes respected, even if those wishes include the withholding of treatment that will save the baby's life.

What is in question here are the judgments that we make about handicapped people, the value we place on their lives and the quality of their lives. What is in question is the quality of the services available for handicapped people in our community, and knowledge based on experience of, for example, individuals with Down's syndrome or spina bifida, some of whom are leading full and enriched lives. What is most in question is how many more people with handicapping conditions could lead fuller and richer lives if we used the knowledge and skills already available to help them to do so.

## References

Crawley, B. (1983), 'The feasibility of trainee committees as a means of self-advocacy in Adult Training Centres in England and Wales.' Unpublished PhD thesis, University of Manchester.

National Development Group for the Mentally Handicapped (1980), *Improving the Quality of Services for Mentally Handicapped People: a checklist of standards*. London, DHSS.

Williams, P. and Shoultz, B. (1982), *We Can Speak for Ourselves: self-advocacy by mentally handicapped people*. London, Souvenir Press.

Wolfensberger, W. and Glenn, L. (1975), *Program Analysis of Service Systems: field manual*. Toronto, National Institute on Mental Retardation.

# 14 Psychotherapy: deliverance or disablement?

*David Smail*

The ethical questions which confront any individual working in the 'helping professions' presumably vary according to that individual's particular situation. For example doctors, nurses, social workers and psychologists find themselves working in contexts which are in several important respects different from each other: in terms, for instance, of the often implicit conceptual and ethical assumptions and pre-occupations of their discipline, and also of the access they may have to the use of formal institutionalised power.

Let me start then, by trying to clarify as far as I can the ways in which my own situation may be helping to shape my view of the ethical issues and dilemmas in psychotherapy. My perspective is that of a non-medical psychotherapist working in the National Health Service, having specialised in psychotherapeutic work within the broader field of clinical psychology. As a psychological therapist in the NHS one has little formal power. Patients are referred by medical practitioners – usually psychiatrists or GPs – and are by and large unable to approach the psychologist directly for treatment. Similarly we have no power to admit patients to or discharge them from hospitals, prescribe drugs, write sick notes for them or otherwise exercise direct institutionalised influence over the material circumstances of their lives. It is not of course that we have no *informal* power; depending on the quality of relations and communications with medical and social work colleagues we may through advice or persuasion be able to bring influence to bear in all these spheres, but I think it is true that we would only seek to do so in a very small minority of cases. Working in the NHS we differ from non-medical psychotherapists in the private sector in that we make no direct charge to our patients for our services. While this may relieve us of temptations to doubtful ethical practices to which private therapists may be exposed, it may also mean that at times we, as well as our patients, are not as clear as we might be about the extent and nature of the contractual arrangement between us. For example, I have no doubt that large institutional organisations like the NHS and the Social

Services at times breed in their employees a rather confused and blurred attitude towards the rights of the individual, which I am sure would be rapidly clarified and sharpened were we paid directly by the individual. I should add emphatically that I do not believe that this is an argument for the dismantling of the welfare state, but rather for those of us who work in such settings to stay alive to the issues involved and not allow the implicit and often unquestioned values of bureaucracy to determine our conduct. (I am thinking, as one example, of the extent to which the pursuit of 'cost-effectiveness' may replace a concern with what is best for the individual patient; or again how confidentiality may be sacrificed in the interests of social engineering in a situation where people have their 'best interests' decided for them by a kind of unseen committee of health and local authority workers.)

My own work, and that of colleagues like me, consists then in a series of face-to-face interviews or sessions with patients in which the focus of attention is how they see and feel about their emotional distress, their relations with others and their relation with the therapist. Though at times we may certainly give practical advice we will rarely attempt to influence patients' lives or circumstances through the use of power.

Now it seems to me self-evident that nobody would undertake this kind of work without having at least an implicit view of what, in some important sense, is *good* for people. For me this means that psychotherapy is centrally a moral undertaking dealing with fundamentally moral issues such as what constitutes psychological well-being, how people should conduct themselves in relation to each other, what stance we take towards emotional distress and psychological pain, where we locate responsibility for the tragic disorder in which so many people live their lives. And yet, with one or two notable exceptions (for example Thomas Szasz, 1978)[1] in their published literature psychotherapists have expended surprisingly little effort in addressing directly the ethical implications of their work, apart from giving some consideration to the desirability or otherwise of manipulating patients through the use of technical procedures ranging from psychoanalytic interpretation to methods of behaviour modification.

The reason for this kind of blindness to the broader moral issues lies, I believe, in the scientific/technological stance which most therapists have chosen to take towards their discipline. In the psychological and psychiatric worlds at least, this stance seems still to embrace mechanistic assumptions that science is value-free, and that the technological applications suggested by scientific observation, theory and experiment are somehow self-justifying unless unworkable for practical reasons (for example that they break the law). The justification which, at least since Freud, psychotherapists have most strenuously sought for their activities has been scientific, and the most damaging charge which can be made against psychotherapeutic theory and practice has been that they are 'unscientific'. As long as what we are doing can in some way be related to scientific credibility, few of us question whether it is right or good. Partly no doubt this is because, until relatively recently, our understanding of mental disorder has been shaped by an analogy with physical illness. The primary task of medicine in this century has been to support its moral position with acceptable scientific evidence that its procedures are effective. Its moral position has not been in question: few would doubt that in general it is right to save life and cure disease, and physicians and patients have been unlikely to find themselves at odds over this proposition, even if nowadays the very effectiveness of some medical procedures has begun to open up areas of moral doubt.

So long then as emotional distress could be seen as mental disease, it has seemed reasonable to leave ethical issues on one side and get on with the job of unravelling the complexities of the, so to speak, mental and behavioural apparatus, in order to find methods of adjusting it so as to reinstate its satisfactory functioning.

There are however a number of signs that our investment in the scientific/technological stance has been too one-sided, and our acceptance of the analogy with physical medicine mistaken.

For one thing the conceptual attack on the 'medical model' in psychiatry which gathered momentum in the 1960s led to the rejection of the view of mental disorder as mental disease by most professional groups working in the broad area of 'mental health' other than psychiatrists themselves. For another thing academic psychology seems in general to have failed to generate theories of human behaviour which could command the allegiance of any scientific community wider than the factions which invented them in the first place. Signs such as these suggest that our mechanistic notions may not be adequate to the task we have set ourselves.

For psychotherapists however, more important than calling into question their reliance on science for the justification of their practice is the actual experience of psychotherapy itself. Now I am sure that a lot of practitioners in this field manage to get by by assuming uncritically the values (buried often almost out of sight) of their professional world as well as of the broader culture in which they operate. It is easy, though I think incorrect, to believe that the psychological theories which inspire therapeutic practice (albeit loosely) are founded on secure scientific foundations, and it is equally easy, and I think almost equally questionable, to feel that one's therapeutic activity is in accord with the best ethical principles. Therapists may often disagree quite vehemently about the *effectiveness* of the means to an end but very rarely about whether the means are themselves justified by the ends. For example, I have found that to question colleagues in clinical psychology about the *rightness* of social engineering to alleviate anxiety is to be met with incredulity; almost anything, it is felt, is justified by the alleviation of 'symptoms' such as anxiety.

However the therapist who attends reflectively to his or her experience of therapy can scarcely fail to be struck by the primacy of moral issues and the inescapability of his or her moral view. It is of course true that, on the basis of their theoretical writings, it would be very difficult to arrive at conceptual generalisations about what psychotherapists do since there are so many different schools of psychotherapy claiming success for their methods on the grounds of widely conflicting theoretical principles. But several students of the psychological therapies agree that, whatever they say they do, experienced therapists tend to set about their work in very similar ways, no matter what dogmatic allegiance they profess.

As I tried to argue in *Psychotherapy: a personal approach*,[2] it seems to me that an open-minded appraisal of what happens in most psychotherapeutic approaches reveals three main stages. The first consists in a, sometimes protracted, process of *negotiation* in which agreement is reached between therapist and patient about the nature of the latter's complaint. The initial complaint of the patient is not taken at its face value but, through the process of negotiation, is given a meaning for the patient in the context of his or her life and relationships which at first he or she did not perceive it to have. For instance many patients come to their therapists complaining of 'symptoms' which they find simply mystifying and unaccountable. Often such symptoms are suggestive to the therapist of anxiety – for example dizziness and nausea, difficulty in breathing, dryness of the mouth, choking sensations, palpitations and so on. The therapist's view then, is likely to be that on occasions the patient is anxious or afraid for what may in fact be very understandable reasons, while the patient's view might be that these symptoms are signs of an inexplicable illness. The analogy with medicine is so far not all that distant: the physically ill patient *expects* the doctor to offer an explanation (diagnosis) for his or her symptoms and will usually accept one unprotestingly as long as it carries a degree of plausibility. However the psychotherapist's suggestion that the patient's symptoms are not simply indications of illness but, say, indications of fear or anxiety, is as likely as not to be met on the patient's part with a kind of hostile disbelief that may take weeks or even months to overcome, so that any analogy with medical diagnosis ends about here. This of course is because many so-called neurotic symptoms constitute the means whereby patients may deceive themselves about the nature of their predicament, which in turn is so intimately related to the consequences of their own conduct that direct recognition of it would involve them in practical and moral self-questioning far more painful than the immediate somatic accompaniments of their anxiety and the bonus these offer for interpretation as illness. To tell people that their rash is due to measles is unlikely to be seen by them as an accusation of moral impropriety, whereas to tell someone that her fainting fits are related to a wish to murder her spouse *is*. It is of course unlikely to be part of the therapist's intention simply to make accusations of moral impropriety; much of the work of negotiating with patients an acceptable account of the meaning of their predicament consists in developing the view that, though it is necessary to become clear about who is doing what to whom in the patient's life, and hence to locate responsibility for all kinds of conduct, it is not part of the therapeutic aim to apportion blame or mete out punishment.

This kind of process of negotiation may go under all sorts of technical names, from 'interpreting the transference' to 'providing a behavioural analysis', but I argue that it is an essentially familiar activity to therapists of a wide variety of persuasions. Its end of course is the achievement of 'insight', but that is not the end of psychotherapy. For having achieved insight – having arrived, that is, at a degree of understanding concerning the reasons for what before seemed inexplicable distress – the patient is then confronted with the significance of being responsible.

The assumption of responsibility I see as the second stage of therapy, bridging and shading into each of the other two. Assuming responsibility for one's own conduct (*not*, let it be noted, for the evils of the world or the inequities of society, which have their own major roles to play in the generation of psychological misery) is the necessary result of seeing how one has come to occupy one's predicament, and the necessary precondition for doing something about it – which latter is the third stage of therapy.

The aim of negotiation is to demonstrate that our past experience and present circumstances give us reasons for being the way we are, but do not inexorably *determine* the way we are. It leads thus to the notion of people as agents, originators of their own conduct in some important respects and whether they *know* it or not. Having acknowledged this degree of responsibility they are then faced with having to do something to alter the actual circumstances of their lives. It is certainly very much easier to see what is wrong – for example that one has helped construct a desperately unhappy and destructive marriage – than to do something about it.

For me the most important concept to invoke at this point is again a fairly clearly ethical one, and that is – courage. Actively to throw oneself into situations which have for years been laden with threat and contemplated with dread takes more than just the application of a few mechanical techniques and a touch of insight: to face those elements in their lives which they have been so assiduously avoiding through the strategies of, say, neurotic anxiety, demands of patients' degrees of courage which they may only be able to muster with the active help and support – in a word, the *encouragement* – of the therapist, who in turn may well find that this is no time to remain seated on a professionally constructed ethical fence. In doing something about his or her predicament the patient takes a leap in the dark, often on the assurance of the therapist that it is safe to do so, that nothing unspeakably awful will happen as the result. What is actually therapeutic of course is the patient's discovery that this is indeed the case, and the consequent learning of new solutions to old problems. Therapists do not operate technically on passive patients in the manner of the surgeon, no matter how tempted they may be to characterise their work in this way, but more like a music teacher and pupil, for example, help patients to place themselves in the best position for finding out for themselves.

In helping patients to understand the reasons for their predicament, to accept responsibility for those aspects of it which originate in their own conduct and to strive actively to do something about it, I do not believe it possible for therapists simply to follow some kind of scientifically established technical manual. Much of the time it is the therapist's *personal* qualities – personal experience and personal judgment, and indeed personally constructed ethical stance – which determines his or her view both of the patient's situation and of what course he or she feels the patient should take in dealing with it. In this sense the therapist is in much the same situation as anyone else who tries to offer support, advice or encouragement to those in distress: there are no objective solutions to the emotional confusions and ethical dilemmas in which so many patients find themselves. The mechanistic bias of psychotherapeutic theory does, it is true, seek to convey a sense precisely of such objectivity in the language used to describe so-called therapeutic techniques. For example, this is particularly obvious in the area of 'behavioural methods' of treatment, in which the jargon of stimulus and response, behavioural 'shaping', 'cognitive restructuring', 'social skills training' and so on, seems to present a picture of a psychological world in which obvious mechanical fault suggests established procedures for the reinstatement of satisfactory functioning. As far as this suggests the possibility of objective value-free therapeutic technique, it is in my view spurious and serves only to further professional mystique and protection from ethical doubt. Human beings evolve a moral world through their own conduct, they do not simply occupy more or less efficiently a world in which standards of behaviour and relationship are objectively established in a way which permits automatic assessment of who is conforming satisfactorily and who is not. Patients and therapists moreover are not insulated from the moral uncertainties of the human situation, but are frequently engaged at their very centre. Often then, there can be no established guidance about what to do in this or that situation: therapists have to make judgments based on their own personal experience and values, and they have to face unflinchingly the fact that they are indeed engaged in the enterprise of *influencing* patients, which they may do for better or for worse. This means, I think, that the justification for therapists' status as *professionals* is not to be found in criteria of technical training or competence or in the scientific adequacy of the theories to which they subscribe. What presumably makes the difference between a helpful layman and a competent psychotherapist consists essentially in little more than the latter's greater *experience* of people in distress. Of course whether or not good is made of that experience is another question, and not one, I think, which has yet been dealt with very convincingly by the psychotherapeutic profession. The criteria we offer the public by which to judge the adequacy of our credentials and our right to practise involve for the most part claims concerning scientific respectability, technical efficiency, academic degrees and approved courses of training. As I have said, I do not believe that these *explicit* criteria take proper account of the essentially moral nature of psychotherapy as an undertaking, although they probably do conceal *implicit* criteria of who is and who is not a competent therapist, which we operate informally and not entirely unsuccessfully.

There was perhaps a time, not all that long ago, when the lay stereotype of the psychotherapist was of a somewhat mysterious figure possessed of an esoteric wisdom and an arcane knowledge of the human psyche. This image, in its day not altogether disavowed by psychotherapists themselves, is now fast disappearing, to be replaced by that of the therapist as competent professional technician, possessor of a repertoire of 'clinical skills' from which judicious selection may be made to suit the needs of the individual case; it is an image which is enthusiastically fostered by many psychotherapists. A recent working party of the British Psychological Society, for example, quoted with approval in its report on psychotherapy a definition of the latter as an:

> informed and planful application of techniques derived from established psychological principles by persons qualified through training and experience to understand these principles and to apply these techniques with the intention of assisting individuals to modify those personal characteristics as feelings, values, attitudes and behaviours... as are judged to be maladaptive or maladjusted.

In my view (which I have elaborated in Smail, 1983)[3] this is far from accurate as a definition of what actually happens in psychotherapy, but serves its purpose in suggesting a view of therapy which many therapists would *like* to be the case and are only too happy for the population at large to believe. In other words it serves the aim of achieving professional credibility as well as going some way towards satisfying a widespread desire in our culture for people to see themselves, when emotionally distressed, as 'dysfunctional' machines.

In adopting the role of the expert technician the therapist, as I have already suggested, apparently steps out of the moral arena and offers his or her services on the basis of a kind of ethically neutral technological efficacy, in principle no different from that which might be claimed by motor mechanics, brain surgeons or indeed psychiatric dispensers of tranquillising drugs or electric shocks. For psychotherapists this stance can, I believe, be maintained only in bad faith or through lack of reflection, but is reinforced through the opportunities it gives for the social legitimation of an ever-increasing, and increasingly prosperous, profession of psychotherapy.

Even though in their activity with individual patients therapists may in fact be working against the expectations set up by this kind of professional pose, its wider effects on the community at large may be positively harmful. As long as people see, and are encouraged to see, their psychological malaise and emotional pain as arising from mechanical fault within them, as essentially unrelated to their place in and contact with the world, as nothing to do with their conduct towards others and others' conduct towards them, or as far as such conduct is viewed simply as the interplay of socially manipulative 'skills', then I believe their ability to evolve any kind of *better* world is stifled. As professional experts, that is, we encourage a view of the world as basically all right or at least as basically unalterable, a world to which people have to *adapt* if they are to get by in it, a world which is so solidly, finitely, objectively *real* that it can be understood, after an appropriate course of study, by experts who can then use their technical knowledge to interpret it to the less expert and modify them to fit more comfortably into it. Being the achievement of an increasingly closed professional group it comes to be accepted that people cannot do this kind of thing for themselves; they become progressively more passive and more unable to understand and criticise their own conduct, the conduct of others and the significance of their own experience.

For example, I have a patient who lives in a terrace council house with four children and a gregarious and periodically alcoholic husband, and neighbours on either side whose noisy adolescent children maintain a kind of constant disruptive feud with her which amounts at times almost to a reign of terror. My patient works every hour God sends, fetching her children to and from school, washing (two of her children are bed-wetters), shopping (her husband is often out of work and she is responsible for budgeting), cooking meals for her own and her husband's family, the numerous members of which may appear, singly or in groups, at any hour of the night up to 3 a.m. expecting a meal. Her children are loving and loved but noisy and demanding. Her husband may come home sober, chatty and concerned or drunk, savagely ironic, brutally demanding food or sex. Until recently (and only because of my encouragement that she should do so) my patient has never, as far as I am aware, *complained* about any of this. What she has done every so often is collapse with exhaustion and anxiety. Taking these 'symptoms' to her doctor at one time she was psychiatrically diagnosed as an 'inadequate personality' and tranquillised so heavily that, by her own account, she scarcely knew what she was doing and as a consequence scalded her hand – now badly scarred – with a saucepan of boiling water. The circumstances of her life, her housing, her neighbours, the demands of her children and of her husband and his family, she has never seen as anything but justifiable, unalterable, simply real and *there*; her experience, as far as I can see, has never suggested to her the possibility of an alternative world. Like her psychiatrist she thinks she is inadequate. As far as *I* can see, as well as being a sensitive and intelligent person she is the most adequate woman I have ever met – anyone else I know would in the face of this strain have died, committed suicide or run away. Before she came to psychotherapy I do not think she had met anyone, professional or otherwise, who had suggested to her anything other than that her occasional failure to operate successfully as a wife and mother in this context was due to some kind of mechanical failure in her ability to cope: she, and not the world, needed changing.

Now I suppose it would be possible to characterise this lady's difficulties as a deficiency in her 'skills' – for example in organising her daily routine, standing up to her husband and his relatives, achieving a measure of discipline with her children; it is certainly true that I have spent a lot of time examining these issues with her. To use this kind of language however would be to obscure the moral issues which confront her: would in fact be tacitly to assume one particular moral position while hiding it behind an apparently objective technical analysis. In fact she has a number of options open to her: to keep going as she is, propped up by pills and the occasional enforced rest; to drive herself to be an even more selfless slave to her family; to agitate for better living conditions both with her family and with the housing authorities and so on; to commit suicide, and so on. When she went to see a locum GP to complain about the painful *sequelae* of a recent operation he readily offered another obvious solution to her difficulties. He had never seen her before but after waving her to a chair riffled through her notes in silence for a few seconds, and then delivered himself of the sentence: 'I see you've had a lot of problems; when are you going to leave him?' It is of course perfectly possible that after due deliberation and negotiation it may seem to a therapist that to encourage a patient to leave a bad marriage would not be inappropriate. More usually, perhaps, one would want to limit one's activity to helping the patient to become aware of the range of choices before her. In this particular case my judgment is that the woman in question has a fundamentally affectionate and warm relationship with her husband, may be partly responsible for occasioning his drinking bouts and would probably not be better off without him. But whether or not this is true, my point is that these are moral questions, that they arise out of circumstances not untypical of those one meets frequently in psychotherapy, and that in practice there is no way in which a therapist can honestly avoid taking up some kind of stance towards them.

As long as therapists make this clear to their patients as well as to themselves, I think they stand a chance of being, at least some of the time, a valuable source of support and encouragement to people in misery and despair who, as things are, have no one else to turn to. It is no doubt sadly ironic that such comfort comes to be dispensed mainly by paid professionals with degrees, qualifications and years of specialised training behind them. However, in so far as we seek to obscure the essentially unpretentious, if morally risky, nature of our calling behind professional mystique, technical mumbo-jumbo and scientific self-righteousness, I think we are likely indirectly to weaken the already failing ability of the wider community to shape its own destiny. This is not to belittle psychotherapy or to suggest that the insights it affords into the reasons for psychological distress and the ways people come to cope with it are inconsiderable. There is no doubt that by acquainting oneself intimately with a particular area of human experience one comes to acquire, if one is able to keep a fairly open mind, a knowledge of some of the principles which operate within it which is unlikely to be developed by just anybody. To pretend that knowledge of such principles should somehow be patented as our own professional property, when in fact it could be laid open for critical public scrutiny and made available for general use, does not seem to me justifiable or in the interests of the moral evolution of our social life.

Presumably therapists are shy of discussing their moral position because of the uncertainties which attach to it. *Any* moral position is debatable, and a therapist's practice, no matter how extensive his or her understanding of human nature or scientific knowledge, must at every moment be open to question and challenge by anybody prepared to reflect upon whether what he or she is attempting to achieve is right. For the sake of a quiet life it is much easier to point to the technical rather than the moral justifications available for therapeutic practice, and much easier to mystify the layman thereby. Many people in our present-day world moreover seem to become paralysed in the face of moral debate: we seem to have an unremitting yearning to change 'oughts' into 'ises', to distance ourselves from the painful necessity of moral reflection and argument – we should on the whole like the world to be mechanically ordered and our 'behaviour' determined by processes outside our responsibility. To raise moral questions and issues is often, it seems, to commit a kind of indecency (as it is in some circles to discuss politics or religion), and is frequently responded to with embarrassment or contempt. If only we could leave everything from parenthood to psychotherapy to the computer: what we need are programs and packages, and training in skills.

In the face of this, no wonder therapists are reticent about what many of them sense is the moral nature of their undertaking. But not all of them are. Those that are not certainly face us with a difficult critical task but, I believe, one we cannot afford to shirk. While we may be put off by the simplistic fervour of some devotees of the 'encounter' movement, or the cloying sentimentality of some, for example American therapeutic gurus, we might be wise to examine carefully the measured arguments of some therapists (as, for example, Peter Lomas in *The Case for a Personal Psychotherapy*[4]) who suggest that, among other things, honesty and love, and even wisdom, have more to do with psychotherapy than professional authority and technique. Things like honesty and love are however extremely difficult to talk about.

## Notes

1   Szasz, T. (1978), *The Myth of Psychotherapy*. Oxford University Press.
2   Smail, D. J. (1978), *Psychotherapy: a personal approach*. London, Dent.
3   Smail, D. J. (1983), 'Psychotherapy and psychology' in D. Pilgrim, ed, *Psychology and Psychotherapy: current trends*. London, Routledge & Kegan Paul.
4   Lomas, P. (1981), *The Case for a Personal Psychotherapy*. Oxford University Press.

# Index

abnormal foetus, 150
abnormality, 45
abortion, 119, 132, 150
  on demand, 40
acceptance, unconditional, 79, 83–4
access
  to services for disabled people, 160–1
  to surrogacy, 115–17
accountability, negative view of, 94, 157–9
action, 15, 17
  liberty of, 51–2
Active Birth Movement, 86
adoption, 110, 113, 115–17
Adult Training Centres, 151–2
advocacy, self, 151–2
Aegeus, 50, 54–5. 59–60
affective neutrality, 2
agape, 17
ageism, 56
agent, 61
agents, people as, 166
agreement, surrogacy, 109–10, 113–15
AIDS, 130
alfa-feto protein test, 92
altruism, 6, 7
ambiguity, 8–9
amniocentesis, 92
anti-welfare policies, 145
anxiety, 165, 170
appeasement, of feelings, 68–73
arguments, moral, 90
Association for Improvements in the Maternity Services, 86
assumptions, moral, 120
authoritarian position, 32
authority, 11, 84
  internalised, external, 78–9
  gracious, 84
autonomy, 33–4, 43, 51–3, 55, 57–60, 62–5, 123
  short-term vs. long-term, 61
aversions, 70, 74

Barclay Committee and Report, 47, 134, 135, 137, 139, 141–5
beliefs
  false, 69
  religious, 73
bereavement, 69, 71–3
  delusions of, 71–2
biological concepts of need, 120
birth
  cascade effect of intervention in, 99
  in a consultant obstetric unit, 98–9, 102
  .in a GP/midwife unit, 101–2
  at home, 39, 99, 102
  place of, 91, 94–103
  style of, 91, 98
  technological, 95
  time of, 92–3
Birth Centre, the, 86
birth experience, 86
Boff, Shannon, 118
Bradshaw, J., 15
Briggs, Lord, 10
*British Births Survey, 1970*, 96
British Medical Association, 35
British Psychological Society, 168
Buber, M., 67

Caesarian section, 89
calling, 4
Campbell, A., 23, 87–8
capacities, natural, 122, 126
care
  affective dimensions of, 23
  antenatal, 91–2
  concept of, 10
  as destructive of the carer, 49
  as detrimental, 47
  as diminishing, 46–7
  holistic, 19
  lay, 10
  medical model of, 27
  maternity, 91–2
  nursing, 10–20, 21–31